Lonely Waters

Proceedings of the International Conference
Music Therapy in Palliative Care
Oxford 1994

Edited by
Colin A Lee

Sobell Publications
Oxford

Sobell Publications
Sir Michael Sobell House
Churchill Hospital
Oxford OX3 7LJ

ISBN 0-9517537-6-2

British Library Cataloguing in Publication Data
A catalogue record for this book is available from the British Library

Printed and bound in Great Britain by
Biddles Ltd, Guildford and King's Lynn

So I'll go down to some lonely waters
Go down where no-one they shall me find
where the pretty small birds do change their voices
And every moment blow blustering wild.

List of Contents

Acknowledgements

Introduction: Music and Dying   3

Part One: Education and Support

Music Therapy Perspectives in Palliative Care Education   13
Susan Porchet-Munro - Switzerland

Music Therapy as a
Supportive Intervention for Professional Care Givers   23
Cathleen O'Neil - America

Part Two: Techniques and Approaches

Songs Written by Palliative Care Patients in Music Therapy   31
Clare O'Callaghan - Australia

Access to Music in Pediatric Bereavement Support Groups   41
Katherine Ryan - America

Music Therapy with
Patients Undergoing Radiation and Chemotherapy   61
Friederike von Hodenberg - Germany

Part Three: Philosophy and Spirituality

Music and Emotion
in Palliative Care: Accessing Inner Resources   71
Deborah Salmon - America

The Role of Music Therapy
in Meeting the Spiritual Needs of the Dying Person   85
Kirstin Robertson-Gillam - Australia

The Voice of the Sounding Bowl   99
Tobias Kaye - England

Why Work With the Dying?   109
Howard Delmonte - England

Part Four: Guided Imagery and Music

Images of AIDS   119
Kenneth E. Bruscia - America

A Journey of Transition with Guided Imagery and Music   125
Denise Erdonmez - Australia

Part Five: Collaboration

The Therapeutic Touch of Music in Palliative Care   137
Mary Rykov - Canada

The Value of Integrating Music Therapy
and Expressive Art Therapy in Working with Cancer Patients   147
Anne Olofsson - Sweden

Working with the Unknown: Music and
Art Therapy with a Young Man with Neimann Picks Disease   153
Gillian Stevens and Hilary Lomas - England

Part Six: Neurological Conditions

On the Vegetative State: Music and Coma Arousal Interventions   163
Mary Elinor Boyle - America

Music Therapy as Part of Assessment and
Treatment for People Living with Huntington's Disease   173
Wendy Magee - England

Music Therapy with Severely Head-Injured Clients   185
Cathy Durham - England

Part Seven: Improvisation

Transcription of an Improvisation
from a Session with a Client Living with HIV   201
Colin A Lee - England

Acknowledgements

Firstly I would like to extend my gratitude to all the presenters and delegates that attended the conference. Thank-you for your support and the long distances many people travelled to attend. Appreciation must be given to all the contributors who responded so well to my editorial comments. Adapting conference papers into a coherent publication is not an easy task, without the support of each author my task would have been considerably more difficult. To Ian Graham, Diana Rivers and Anne Green for your final comments. The three key-note speakers, Susan Porchet-Munro, Kenneth E Bruscia, David Aldridge. They all gave inspiring papers that added richness to an already diverse programme. To my colleagues in the Study Centre, Ann Champion, Lorraine Gibson and Carol Glasson, thank-you for your support from the time the conference was first proposed, for being there when I had my many crises and for persuading me regularly not to cancel. To Robert Twycross for being a quiet but constant support and providing the exciting opening remarks. To Susan Boreham without whom neither the conference nor these proceedings would have been possible. Thanks for your constant hard work, dedication and for being professional as well as making me laugh. To the volunteers who assisted at the conference, who provided such a beautiful display of flowers and those who helped with the furniture removal on the final afternoon. To Cathleen O'Neil who arrived the day before the conference and gave me encouragement whilst organising the last minute tasks. Lastly I would like to thank all my colleagues in day care for your constant love and listening.

This book is dedicated to Maria, Sue and all those patients who died at Sobell House during the summer of 1984.

Introduction

Music and Dying

Colin A Lee
Oxford, UK

While the International Conference: Music Therapy in Palliative Care held at Sir Michael Sobell House Hospice, Oxford may have seemed small in comparison to other more established music therapy events, it hopefully provided a forum for therapists working within this relatively small field to share clinical practice. I think one of the reasons that the conference attracted such widespread and diverse delegates (see fig 1) was the comparatively small position it holds within music therapy. In relative terms, interest from allied professionals appeared to be considerable. This, coupled with the problems of defining a clear approach that differentiates the work from, but includes it within, the overall umbrella of music therapy produced a clear need for sharing. Using music with the dying is a demanding process; in psychotherapeutic terms issues of countertransference become multi-layered and complex. Perhaps it was for this reason that delegates preferred to experience seven hours of presentations per day, rather than have a programme with parallel-running papers.

My memories of the conference are tinged with excitement and dread. As all music therapists who have organised conferences will hopefully recognise, there is a difficult balance to be maintained between providing a forum for the new and innovative and dealing with the practicalities necessary for providing a smooth running event. That the conference was small meant the presentations had to take place within the study centre of the hospice itself. The diverse nature of the papers, however, provided a range of clinical approaches that more than balanced the problems of space. Certainly in England there has never been such an international spread of work available. There were papers that infuriated some whilst inspiring others. I have always been committed to such openness of dialogue as essential to the furtherance of music therapy. While the contribution of this conference to music therapy as a whole may be small, hopefully it provided a forum where there could be a willingness to share, learn and respect our differences within a field that is rapidly growing.

Figure One - Analysis of Delegates Attending Conference

	Music Therapists	Allied Professionals
England	19	14
Norway	1	1
Switzerland	1	0
Germany	4	2
Belgium	1	0
Sweden	1	3
USA	6	0
Canada	2	0
Australia	5	1
Japan	3	1
	43	22

Loss and Endings

Offering music to people who are faced with a terminal diagnosis is one of the most challenging but powerful experiences a music therapist can have. What can music offer someone who is facing the end of their life? How can the music therapist hope to find the musical honesty and openness necessary for such potentially painful and demanding work? One of the first things a music therapist must face in palliative care is the ability to adapt the therapeutic approach for the client's needs. This may mean playing the simplest of musical activities; it may mean listening; it may mean silence; or it may require a subtle and intricate improvisational dialogue. Whatever route is taken, listening is at the heart of music therapy.[1,2,3] When working with dying people there is a sense of attending at many levels through music and beyond. In silence the client can lead the therapeutic apex toward more in-depth pauses or return to musical expression and the living force of music. It is through the intensities of listening that the therapist can 'be there',[4] not as a esoteric concept but in a real sense as an accompanist throughout the stages of the dying process.

I recently arranged the funeral of a friend who died of AIDS. As his illness progressed so our relationship deepened. We had worked together as client and therapist some six years earlier and since the end of our therapeutic relationship had become close friends. There came the recognition as his health deteriorated, that this would be the last person I knew who would die from a community of clients, colleagues and friends whom I first met during my time at London Lighthouse (a centre for people facing the challenge of AIDS).[5] His eventual death acted as a catalyst in coming to terms with the numerous losses I have experienced during my work as music therapist both at Lighthouse and now Sir Michael Sobell House. Alongside my grief for Tony I developed an intense alliance with a female client after only one session. There seemed to be an innate understanding of her crisis and our quickening relationship. Musically our involvement was simple and came from a knowledge based on the union of creative spirits. Whilst this situation in itself is not unique in palliative care (over half my work involves on average three sessions or less), the instinctive depth involved often leaves one feeling estranged. Whilst our time had been complete in itself, I was left to make sense of our mutual sense of 'being there' within the bounds of a music therapy encounter. The intimacy in both relationships seemed independent of frequency or time. On reflection I realised that my sense of loss was equal for both people; that my potential bereavement was a crucial part of staying alongside the dying process. I believe that allowing this sense of continuity is essential in being straightforward as a music therapist and human being.

That is not to suggest that music therapy in palliative care is in essence more difficult than other areas of music therapy. Rather I would suggest its practice needs greater flexibility than is available from one clinical method or approach. There is an implicit awareness for music therapists working in palliative care that all approaches are valid and necessary. The therapist must be able to call upon a whole range of therapeutic interventions if the needs of the client are to be fully met. Perhaps this would explain why music therapists in palliative care have felt the need to meet and share. The first symposium in 1989[6] collated work from Australia, Canada, America and Switzerland. The areas covered highlighted the need for an eclecticism of approaches that is hopefully continued and extended through the publication of these proceedings.

Having recently completed a piece of writing that is emotionally honest and non-academic,[7] I came to the conclusion that when describing music and dying one cannot be totally detached. That professional assessment needs to be carefully placed alongside honesty and human clarity. I remember struggling to find a clear and balanced description of our work. This often painful process highlighted the need to retain a sense of self within the bounds of such emotive, charged material. After eight years working in palliative care I still encounter a daily essence of the unknown. Every new client I meet provides a new therapeutic process, a new approach to my work and a sense that I am indeed starting anew. It is the paradox of the life force of music that it allows endings and death to survive alongside growth and life in an immediacy of music and silence that is often mysterious. The following papers highlight a diversity that is at the heart of music therapy in palliative care. There is a core that connects all the work presented: a belief that music can affect the expression of loss.

Endings are a crucial dynamic in all areas of music therapy.[8] Every beginning is the herald to an ending. The number of sessions may be limited or ongoing. Whichever approach is taken, the emphasis of the therapeutic process is toward resolution. In palliative care endings are concentrated and complex. They are, however, perhaps more similar than one would at first imagine to the endings faced by many music therapists in other areas of work. The culmination is essentially different, whilst the experience could be seen to be similar. Endings require an acceptance of what has gone before and how this will affect the future. The ending must be acknowledged by therapist and client, allowing a natural disintegration of roles. How often will therapists at the final analysis gladly relinquish their professional role in favour of parting on less formal terms? There can be a sense of relief that the formalities of the relationship are now complete and that in the final moments there can be a clearer sense of two people, rather than therapist and client. It is this point of ending with dying people that for me is the most crucial, spiritual and fundamentally true aspect of my work. Often at this juncture music is not appropriate. There is a consummation of the relationship that goes beyond, but which has been dependent on, the musical expression of the self.

The search for the musical soul in the face of death and dying can be an enigmatic experience. Many clients will attempt to describe the feelings that have been engendered through music. Some are successful whilst others acknowledge their inability to express themselves in words and allow the music to speak for itself. What music is adequate to express the enormity of dying? How can the music therapist help the client toward a musical translation that enables growth in the face of death? In truth the task is impossible yet simple. Through trusting the moment the therapist may, at times, enter the world of the client and open up a musical essence that reflects the pain of dying. Music however can only provide that which is instinctive in life: it is man-made, and of this world. Beyond lies the relationship and the culmination of music therapy implicit in palliative care. The endings held in such great music as JS Bach's B Minor Mass, Beethoven's string quartet op. 127, Schoenberg's opera 'Moses and Aaron' or more recently 'Passion' by Sondheim, are artistic extensions of these feelings. These examples are a part of an ever-growing realisation of the spiritual nature of music that is being directly extended by such present-day composers as Arvo Part and John

6

Tavener. We should take note of these composers and their music. Their works survive as a testimony to the struggles of music in depicting endings in the face of life.

Cultural and Clinical Differences

International and theoretical divides in clinical practice are as prevalent today as when music therapy was first established.[9] In theory music therapists celebrate their differences, with respect for approaches different to their own. Is there not still, however, a sense of suspicion that one technique ultimately holds a greater sense of truth, and that by accepting another's principles the original will somehow become diluted? My work in palliative care has shown that a song, a prerecorded piece of music, a session of Guided Imagery with Music or an intense improvisational encounter can all have equally profound therapeutic effects. As a music therapist taught mainly in improvisation I concentrated initially on extending my knowledge of that approach. Alongside, and with equal emphasis, I have studied new skills that are different from my initial training. The reason for this self-imposed learning, and why I believe music therapy in palliative care can bridge the divide between clinical approaches, is simple: the needs of the client demand a complete panorama of techniques.

I recently had the privilege to work alongside Audree O'Connell, Associate Professor of Music Therapy at the University of the Pacific.[10] For her sabbatical term she worked with me and at a hospice in Ireland. Whilst our techniques were ostensibly different we immediately understood each other's professional intent. There was a bond between us that stemmed from a respect for our differences and the problems of working with dying people. During our time we worked intensely together with two clients. Apart from the pleasure I felt in having a colleague within the bounds of my practice, we both became fascinated with the potential for learning from our clinical polarities. We appraised the sessions themselves and set hypothetical situations from past experience. By discussing and comparing how we would approach various incidents we were able to view the therapeutic sphere, so to speak, from many different perspectives. Through our in-depth analyses I learnt much about the possibilities of choice and the importance of offering a wide range of music for clients.

The reader will hopefully experience in these proceedings a diversity of techniques and approaches. I hope that you will find empathy with many of the papers and that you will disagree with others. Being eclectic does not mean that one need not be selective. There are various topics presented and conclusions drawn in these papers that I personally do not agree with. They are so far removed from my ideologies that it would be foolish to try and include their views within my practice. It has been my experience throughout this conference and subsequent editing that it is the provocative papers that perhaps contain the most fascinating learning. The editor's job is to present individual voices within an overall continuity of style. This has not always been an easy task with clinical boundaries, variations of definition and stylistic expression. I have tried always to present the authors' ideas unbiased, and provide the reader with a sense of the forward-looking that was so inherent during the conference itself. I have added comments to certain papers that will hopefully help to place their content within the context of the proceedings as a whole. The differences in these papers then are a testament to the broad range of possibilities when working with the dying.

Editing and Structure

The problems in editing material from a diversity of clinical and cultural backgrounds as already discussed, meant constant reviewing for each paper and the publication as a whole. National idiosyncratic spellings have been left intact whilst certain colloquialisms and aspects of 'music therapy speak' have wherever possible been clarified. Hopefully the lay-reader as well as experienced music therapist will be able to follow the theme of each paper.

The following papers were presented at the conference but not submitted for publication in these proceedings:

- Music Therapy for Cancer Patients at Vidar Hospital. Hika Osika, Sweden.

- Arts Therapies Incorporated in the Care of People Affected by HIV and AIDS. Lutz Neugebauer, Germany.

- 'In Retrospect, In Prospect': Creative Music Therapy with Those Who are Living with, or Who are Affected by HIV and AIDS. Nigel Hartley, England.

- Spirituality, Hope and Creativity.[11] David Aldridge, Germany.

- Where Words Fail Music Takes Over: A Collaborative Study by a Music Therapist and a Counsellor in the Context of Cancer Care. Leslie Bunt, England.

The remaining 18 papers have been arranged in seven sub-sections. Part one describes the need for music therapists to be involved within palliative care education and support. Both papers focus on the complex needs of the health care professional when exploring personal difficulties in the face of continued loss, and the impact this has on continuing education. Part two explains three different clinical approaches, to work with dying patients and bereaved children drawing mainly on the use of songs. Part three focuses on aspects of philosophy and spirituality. Each paper holds a different perspective: from clinical work and personal thoughts through to the philosophical speculations of a wood-craftsman turned instrument-maker. Part four reveals the powerful therapeutic process available through Guided Imagery and Music. The transcription of sessions with a woman with Motor Neurone Disease further adds to the growing literature of GIM that provides a real sense of the process.[4] Collaboration using other arts therapies and allied complementary techniques is an aspect of music therapy in palliative care that is being developed. In part five the authors describe their alliance with other approaches and the effect this has had on their practice. Part six is concerned with the consequences of using music with people who have neurological problems. Whilst these papers might at first seem to have the least connection with palliative care, they highlight the need for an intricate practice when working with people in comas and with slowly degenerating conditions.

Finally, part seven includes a complete transcription of an improvisation from a session with a client living with HIV. The original presentation offered three musical examples from a young man recently bereaved. This substitution nevertheless, supports the idea of experiencing music in music therapy without in-depth interpretation or evaluation.

The conference included numerous musical examples that highlighted the therapeutic process at many levels. This is reflected in the scores presented here as essential to the text. Due to financial constraints we were unable to provide audio recordings of the music itself; although this is an aspect of the presentation of music therapy that is now taking greater precedence.[3,7] Hopefully the scores will go some way towards highlighting the importance of including musical examples when describing the approach of music therapy in palliative care.

References

1. Amir D (1995). On Sound, Music, Listening and Music Therapy. In: Kenny (ed). *Listening, Playing, Creating: Essays on the Power of Sound*. State University of New York Press.

2. Langdon GS (1995). The Power of Silence in Music Therapy. In: Kenny (ed). *Listening, Playing, Creating: Essays on the Power of Sound*. State University of New York Press.

3. Ansdell G (1995). *Music for Life. Aspects of Creative Music Therapy with Adult Clients*. Jessica Kingsley Publishers, London and Philadelphia.

4. Bruscia KE (1995). Modes of Consciousness in Guided Imagery and Music (GIM): A Therapist's Experience of the Guiding Process. In: Kenny (ed). *Listening, Playing, Creating: Essays in the Power of Sound*. State University of New York Press.

5. Cantacuzino M (1993). *Till Break of Day. Meeting the challenge of HIV and AIDS at London Lighthouse*. Heinemann, London.

6. Martin JA (1989). The Next Step Forward. *Music Therapy with the Terminally Ill*. Proceedings from a Symposium for Music Therapists Working in Palliative Care. Calvary Hospital, Bronx, New York.

7. Lee CA (In Press). *Music at The Edge. The Music Therapy Experiences of a Musician Living with AIDS*. Routledge, London and New York.

8. Lee CA (1991). Foreword: Endings. *Journal of British Music Therapy*; *5(1)*: 3-4.

9. Bunt L (1994). *Music Therapy. An Art Beyond Words*. Routledge, London and New York.

10. Hanser SB, Larson SD & O'Connell AS (1983). The effect of music on relaxation of expectant mothers during labor. *Journal of Music Therapy*; 22: 50-58.

11. Aldridge D (1995). Spirituality, hope and music therapy in palliative care. *Arts in Psychotherapy*; *22(2)*: 103-9.

Part One

Education and Support

Music Therapy Perspectives in Palliative Care Education

Susan Porchet-Munro
Birchwill, Switzerland

This paper suggests that palliative care education needs an experiential component with a focus on introspective awareness, emotional reaction patterns and abilities for emotional expression. Music therapy perspectives and techniques can be key elements within such a component.

Introduction

One may want to question if this topic will have the same consequences as the first talk about music therapy in terminal care to an international audience, on the occasion of the Second International Conference in Montreal in 1980. The fact, however, that an international group of music therapists working with the terminally ill in various parts of the world gathering at this time, gives rise to a daring hope that fourteen years from now there may be a gathering of music therapists involved in Palliative Care Education! Music therapists have something important to offer in terms of education in palliative care. Provocative professional forward-thinking needs to be part of music therapy development.

The reflections are related to my personal connection as therapist, educator and consultant in the development of palliative care over the last seventeen years.

When I joined the Royal Victoria Hospital in Montreal in 1977, the service had only been in existence for two years. Education was considered as important a commitment as patient care and research. Given the pioneer status of this first palliative care service in a university teaching hospital and the 'novelty' of music therapy in the field, I not only had to present the scope and implications of music therapy in various teaching contexts, but also had to be involved in the development of palliative care teaching tailored to groups of professionals as well as lay persons.

Given my professional background, it seemed obvious to propose (and demonstrate where possible) experiential teaching methods. These included music therapy and creative arts activities because palliative care philosophy suggests the need for introspection and heightened personal awareness.

Through my observations at that time, I was led to the conviction that education in palliative care needed to address a specific learning about emotional experience and expression. These conclusions came from sitting in many staff support meetings, intended to help care-givers with the emotional impact of the work. Whenever emotional issues in patient care seemed to influence the staff and staff relations, the discussions invariably circled around the needs and emotions of patients and families, and rarely those of staff. Feelings were rarely expressed and shared. Team members seemed to be experts on how *patients* should feel, share and express! The suggestion to use non-verbal, creative techniques to address deeper concerns - at that time - was not considered opportune or appropriate. The ways of dealing with emotions openly in a group seemed blocked.

On the other hand, interviews for a study on burnout which were carried out with the same caregivers, showed that these, even in the confidence of a one to one interview, would talk only reluctantly about their dilemmas and the emotional impact of their work. These interviews revealed, however, that the front line realities of caring for the terminally ill patient *are* difficult. (To quote one example):

> *"You know, this touches you, this hits you. For example, let's say there are Mondays where I am in great shape and when I've made my rounds and it took three hours, three and a half sometimes, even four, it is not confusing, you know, you see that it touched you. You are like the guy who received five or six big blows, do you understand? Two or three in the teeth, four in the stomach, do you understand, this touches ..."*.[1]

Palliative Care Education and the Emotional Impact of Terminal Care Work

Did palliative care teaching programmes consider and include experiential components with a focus on such highly emotional experiences?

This question was pursued in an MA thesis.[2] In it, the nature and meaning of care/caring and terminal care were reflected upon in depth. The models for the education of healthcare professionals (nurses, doctors, various therapists), and educational programmes within hospices in particular, were carefully screened to see if such programs considered *experiential* teaching components and modalities which particularly addressed and fostered *introspective awareness, emotional reaction patterns and abilities for emotional expression.*

The screening showed that health care education in general was then (and mostly still is today) based on the medical education model. This values cognitive learning highly and largely ignores issues of affect and emotion in terms of the patient and the caregiver.

Hospice education programmes underlined the complex emotional needs of patients and families as well as the potential for burnout and the need for staff support. The importance for the caregiver of exploring personal attitudes and feelings with regard to death, dying and stress was acknowledged. The major emphasis, however, in these programs remained on the acquisition of knowledge, skills and techniques *necessary to meet the patient's needs more efficiently.* Whilst the 'whole person approach' was promoted as central in terms of care for the terminally ill patient, it never seemed central for the education and development of the caregiver. Teaching modules based on cognitive learning far outweighed those tailored to experiential learning and the expression of emotional issues.

The conclusion of my thesis was that palliative care education should be based on a 'whole person' educational model; and t   hat music therapy and creative arts techniques could make a valuable contribution, because they foster introspective awareness and insight. These could function as an emotional, effective teaching component. At the time, my work was received with scepticism and even irritation, paralleling the documentation on the suffering of caregivers mentioned earlier.

Important Developments

In recent years, palliative care education has become separate from other areas of care. The Canadian Palliative Care Curriculum[3] divided the specific goals and objectives into those which primarily reflect knowledge, skills *and* attitudes. The curriculum acknowledged the importance of individual encounter as having equal weight with knowledge and skill. The curriculum, however, offered no suggestions as to how this might be addressed or taught.

An international conference - the first with the specific focus of palliative care education - took place in Brussels in 1991. Curriculum content did not seem to engender much discussion or argument. Many presenters, however, underlined the need for an educational programme which would nurture astute interpersonal skills and afford the opportunity for introspection on the part of the caregiver and a confrontation with issues of anxiety, grief and helplessness. Still, no suggestions as to how this might be achieved were put forward.

In 1992, the European Association for Palliative Care published a survey on the current status of professional education in palliative care. It reflected the diversity of programmes and programme development at national and international levels. It also outlined programmes of study in more detail. The one for Training at Senior Registrar Level (Great Britain) specified that doctors would need to acknowledge their emotional stress and the stress of other team members. There is an acknowledgement that 'teaching and learning of palliative medicine lends itself to a particularly wide range of educational methods'.[4] In terms of experiential learning, tutorials, small group discussions, project work, portfolio learning, role play and video observation are suggested. No mention is made of creative arts approaches. These changes in the expectations, stressing a focus on attitudes which nurture compassionate care as well as the need for knowledge and skill, were significant.

At the Second Congress of the European Association for Palliative Care in 1992, the emphasis became more pronounced. Dr Neil MacDonald, talking about priorities in education and research focused on an important issue. He pointed out that in academic circles the opinion is not uncommon that 'palliative care is not considered of university standard', and he challenged listeners to create an opening in academic circles for the specific goals of palliative care education. He charged delegates to consider 'an educational mission' for a change in attitude. He suggested 'interactive teaching programmes' without further definition. He clearly spelled out however, that 'conventional educational methods stressing the mastery of a defined body of facts, often presented by lecturers to a passive group of students, will no longer suffice'.[5]

Dr Derek Doyle (St Columba Hospice, Edinburgh), at the same conference, presented some sobering facts which challenged expectations in connection with emotional teaching components. His remarks referred to the topic of the education for doctors: in five years of training, the average time allotted to the subject of palliative care is 6.75 hours! Dr Doyle asked provocative questions about this: What should be taught in this time? Heightened awareness? General principles? Technical details? He underlined the importance of the need for time to experience, to reflect, to consider the meaning of suffering and its relationship to - but he also highlighted the fact that such topics were highly questionable in terms of 'academic acceptability'. This indicated that the need for experiential learning at introspective levels had been defined by experienced hospice care, but was also a poignant reminder that such concepts were considered questionable in terms of academic acceptability and standards.

A further topic, not normally referred to in palliative care circles, is now being addressed. Dr R Schaerer,[6] Professor of Oncology in Grenoble, France, has spoken about the suffering of doctors who work in terminal care and are confronted with the death of patients. He presented a study[6] on this topic in which 81 of 130 General Practitioners replied: 86% readily agreed with the words 'suffering of the doctor'

The three main dominating feelings mentioned in connection with the care of the patient in the terminal phase were:

- sadness: 90%
- helplessness: 89%
- failure: 82%

A Need Confirmed

Based on the above statements, the suffering of the caregiver does exist and is openly admitted. This is at a time when not only palliative care and the development of palliative medicine, but also healthcare in general is at a cross-roads. There are more cancer patients every year and the number of Aids patients is growing. There are more ethical dilemmas in medicine than ever before and even less money. The pioneer days of Palliative Care are over. Programmes have developed, still run or have closed. The focus today is on palliative medicine and its recognition as a speciality within the medical 'arena'.

As is usual at times of reassessment and stocktaking, new demands emerge. This is exactly what happened when palliative care was put into the perspective of the future. Relevant to the topic of this paper, one of the emerging demands stated was: 'we must recognize the pivotal goal of reducing fear and helplessness on the part of the professional'.[7] 'Reducing fear and helplessness' - does this not require personal introspection, confrontation with emotions, struggles, anxieties and limitations? Does this not require the ability to touch on issues of feeling, perceiving and emotional turmoil and to find means for expression?

Scott[7] realized that his request had consequences for education when he stated: 'we need rapid sophistication of educational techniques for palliative care education'! This statement, however, is not followed by a definition of sophisticated educational techniques, or by other concrete suggestions.

Music Therapy Perspectives

Music therapy perspectives offer principles which share essential characteristics with the concept of 'whole person education':

- In music therapy, individuals learn, grow and discover through creative endeavour. This helps to bypass intellectual control, heighten awareness and facilitate non-verbal and verbal expression

- In music therapy, individuals gain personal depth/insight through multisensory experience

- Music therapy offers a space to explore the interplay between control and letting go

- Music therapy encourages the discovery of inner resources

- Music therapy presents opportunities to experience being/feeling in the moment: it offers a space which permits and fosters encounter with 'negative' issues such as fears, anxiety, anger and pain

- Music therapists believe that human beings have an incredible potential for growth

Music Therapy Techniques

In essence, music therapy techniques facilitate the access to deeper awareness, altered perception and consciousness. They call upon imagination, fantasy, and creativity and provide a bridge between the rational and the irrational. They offer ways of venturing into previously unexplored depths and help bypass intellectual control and analysis for the sake of realistic acknowledgement of inner conflicts and discord.

Music functions as a catalyst in activities which may include:

- music playing: for intra- or interpersonal expression, group experience on a non-verbal level or fun

- music listening: to access associations, emotions and images

- music assisted activities:
  - movement (which can free the body before the mind)
  - collage (which lets inner images take a visible form)
  - sculpting with clay and sand (which permits introspective reflection while lingering over symbolic meaning)

The context (type of course/participant) determines the choice of musical or thematic material as well as the mode in which music is experienced. The extent to which such musical experience is recounted or worked through verbally depends on given situations. At times, musical experience may enhance and nurture verbal expression, thus making the inexpressible expressible, or at other times, it may make verbal exchange obsolete, in that musical content itself rendered an issue tangible, significant and understandable. Individuals encounter themselves and others on a different plane when they are involved in creative activities, and they live the ebb and flow between the tangible and intangible. In this way symbolic and emotional content of experience begins to be valued as highly as rational understanding and cognition.

Such learning enhances the sensitivity necessary with regard to:
- listening
- silence
- the broaching of sensitive topics
- the importance of symbolic language
- the importance of the uniqueness of the individual
- the search for meaning

Delineation Education/Therapy

It is important to underline the fact that the use of music therapy techniques to address emotional concerns in education needs to be clearly tailored. The person who proposes the use of such modalities should be as highly skilled as the physician who teaches pharmacological and medical knowledge, or the nurse who lectures on nursing assessment and care. The teacher/music therapist has to be as comfortable and competent with the 'pain' of the caregiver as the physician is with the pain of the patient. The therapist has to have as much respect for the caregiver as for the patient. They need to have the competence and humility to honor education as distinct from therapy whilst recognizing the need to suggest therapy when appropriate. Any individual may wish to use elements of music in teaching. The highly potent nature of this medium, however, should not be

19

ignored. If music therapy techniques are to pave the way for in-depth processes and introspection as part of education, they should be initiated by a well-trained therapist with good teaching skills.

Music Therapy and Creative Arts Perspectives in Practice

In 1992, under the sponsorship of the Swiss Cancer League, a pilot teaching programme in palliative care addressed a multidisciplinary group of healthcare professionals (15 nurses working in various settings, two physicians, one social worker, one chaplain, one physiotherapist).[8] Curriculum content was based on internationally accepted guidelines including topics such as:

- death, society and palliative care
- the management of pain
- pharmacological and non-pharmacological supportive measures in symptom control
- communication, counselling and accompaniment
- loss and grief
- multidisciplinary teamwork
- pastoral care
- ethical principles and decision-making

The programme was spread over a year, in teaching units of two to three days. This timing allowed for adequate coverage of theoretical material, as well as in-depth personal and professional reflection. To underline the fundamental need for multidisciplinary teamwork and create a model in palliative care the team of tutors included a nurse clinician, two physicians, a family therapist, chaplain and music therapist. Besides the transmission of information and work within groups, emphasis was placed on the use of music therapy and creative arts techniques as teaching methods to enhance introspective awareness, to highlight emotional reaction patterns, and to facilitate expression. Evaluation mid-point, at the end, and six months later examined how the teaching components contributed towards the learning experience. The use of creative techniques clearly made an important contribution (tables with evaluation I,II,III).

Music Therapists and Palliative Care Teaching

In the editorial to the thematic issue on 'Palliative Care 2000' of the *Journal of Palliative Care*, Roy,[9] in looking at the challenges facing palliative care in the future, suggested identifying its central problems by asking the question who

20

was going to teach what to whom. In his pilot project, the concept of this educational programme required the collaboration of a multidisciplinary team, where each tutor with his/her professional background had equal responsibility and input.

Multidisciplinary teaching is often suggested; however, music therapists are rarely mentioned as members of the teaching team. While many music therapists are often called upon to familiarise staff with their approaches and techniques, the question remains why music therapy is not considered in formal curriculum development. This is despite the fact that its contribution to patient care and informal teaching is recognized as significant.

As palliative medicine is struggling to find a place within traditional medical education, it already faces questions about what is and will be 'academically acceptable' and what should be taught in the few hours allotted.[10] To speak in addition of affective learning and emotional components as part of academic education may be regarded as heresy. The thought of a music therapist teaching students in established medical schools is provocative. If palliative care is at a cross-roads and already in the process of identifying the issues of education for the future, this may be the time to examine the fundamental concept of 'who is going to teach what to whom'. It may mean considering a truly multidisciplinary faculty for curriculum development and teaching or, at least, the recognition of less orthodox teaching methods alongside familiar ones in order to address the suffering of future caregivers.

At a time when much of the theoretical and functional knowledge could be transmitted by video documents or through thematic manuals, it seems important to spend the limited teaching hours on matters of relationship and communications as well as on emotional experience. This would take the same courage as the initiation of palliative care or music therapy did in the 1970s. The result of such a choice, however, may make as important a difference to the competence of healthcare professionals in their work with patients and their coping with personal struggles and suffering as the development of symptom control and palliative care has made to the suffering of terminally ill patients over the past twenty years.

Conclusion

Music therapy, over the last years, has gained recognition within palliative care.[11] Given their professional background and the nature of their work, music therapists working in palliative care are aware of emotional issues, and of the needs and suffering of patients. They use their skills and techniques to encourage introspective awareness and to provide opportunities to experience and express issues of feeling, perceiving, emotional turmoil or uncertainty. In the future, these music therapists will need to have the courage to seek opportunities where they can draw attention to the fact that music therapy perspectives and techniques not only have an important contribution to make in terms of patient care, but can contribute significantly to palliative care education as well. They will have to demonstrate convincingly, that, whilst music therapy and creative arts techniques may only be one component of education in palliative medicine, this component may be the only one able to enhance and permit the much needed 'affective' learning within medical education.

References

1. Lambert P (1984). *L'Etude du Phenomène de l'Epuisement Professionnel chez le Personnel des Unités de Soins Palliatifs*. Unpublished MA Thesis, Université de Montréal, pp 124-125.

2. Munro S (1986). *The Education of the Health Care Professional in Terminal Care in the Light of the Emotional Impact of the Nature of the Work*. Unpublished MA Thesis, McGill University, Montreal.

3. Macdonald N (1991). The Canadian Palliative Care Curriculum.

4. European Association for Palliative Care (1992). *Survey on the Current Status of Professional Education in Palliative Care*. p 25.

5. Macdonald N (1993). Priorities in education and research in palliative Care. *Palliative Medicine*; *7(1)*: 65-76.

6. Schaerer R (1993). Suffering of the doctor linked with the death of patients. *Palliative Medicine*; *7(1)*: 27-37.

7. Scott J (1992). Palliative Care Education in Canada: Attacking Fear and Promoting Health. *Journal of Palliative Care*; *8(1)*: 47-53.

8. Porchet-Munro S (1993). Pilotprojekt: Interdisziplinäre Weiterbildung in Palliative Care. *Bulletin Suisse du Cancer*; *3*: 83-84.

9. Roy D (1992). Palliative Care 2000: Where do we start? *Journal of Palliative Care*; *8(1)*: 3-4.

10. Doyle D (1992). Training for Doctors in Palliative Care. Seminar at the Second European Congress on Palliative Care, Brussels.

Music Therapy as a Supportive Intervention for Professional Care Givers

Cathleen O'Neil
California, USA

This paper will outline the development of a music therapy support group for hospice care givers. Additional supportive interventions will be discussed in the hopes of inspiring other music therapists to initiate similar groups, thereby broadening our field.

The music therapy support group was designed to address the stresses experienced by staff members working in palliative care. Among the most common are:

- Working with patients in pain
- Dealing with families in crisis
- Caring for patients who are not going to get well
- Caring for patients who are grossly disfigured
- Exposure to unusual and distressing deaths
- Grief and loss
- Saying 'goodbye' to patients, to families, to other staff
- Not being able to 'let go'
- Confronting one's own mortality
- Demands made by one's supervisors and administrators, including increased case load in rigid time constraints
- Demands made by difficult patients
- Demands of one's personal life

Most care givers at the Southern California Kaiser Permanente Hospice had been in the field for a long time. They had been exposed to these stresses with little opportunity to deal with their feelings. Each believed that they were alone in what they were feeling. In reality, most team members were coping or dealing with the same fears and feelings as their co-workers. When given the opportunity to share in a group setting, members discovered that they were not alone. Self-esteem was enhanced and group members were able to recommit to high quality care for dying patients.

After a number of years working as the music therapist on the hospice team, I was asked to provide music therapy for the facility's twelve home care nurses and home health aids (throughout this paper I will refer to the participants as nurses). This group met for one-and-a-half hours twice a month. In order to accommodate changing schedules and administrators, the time and length of the group varied. Attendance was not mandatory although highly encouraged among group members. Staff support was viewed as a necessity and was incorporated within the working day. Staff members were paid for their time.

The goals established for the group were:

- To increase self-esteem
- To increase self-awareness
- To develop communication skills
- To promote a sense of 'team'

Activities were developed to achieve these goals and to allow staff members to receive support and encourage others. By recognizing strengths and incorporating them into songs, group members received the validation of their peers. The refrain from Helen Reddy's 'I am Woman' is an ideal place to substitute the strength of a participant. 'I am STRONG, I am INVINCIBLE', became 'I am GENTLE, I am CARING'. I would often sing a refrain, changing one or two words. 'I Believe in Music', by Mack Davis, is powerful when one substitutes a person's name for the words 'music' or 'love'. During groups I made it a point to maintain eye contact while singing to each individual. On many occasions, staff members expressed pleasure and appreciation for these personal moments of recognition.

Over time, as self-respect was enhanced the focus shifted to the esteem of the entire group. From the beginning, the group chose themes that expressed particular feelings. These were as different as the moods and fluctuating energy of the group. When nurses began to carry bleepers, artist Billy Towne's lyrics to 'Never on Sunday' became 'Oh you can BEEP me on a Monday, a Monday, a

Monday' etc. Spontaneous word substitutions kept expression flowing and the group lively.

Nurses laughed easily and were at times very playful. However, these moods could change quickly. The group could become subdued and tearful as music elicited feelings, especially of grief and loss. One song which remained a favorite and seemed to strengthen the participants was 'One Day at a Time' by Marijohn Wilkin and Kris Kristofferson. When one nurse was hospitalized, the group made a tape recording of this song as a gift to speed her recovery. Afterwards, tapes of this song and others were made for each nurse to be kept in the car. These songs not only expressed feelings and gave hope, they fostered a sense of control.

Playing instruments gave each member an opportunity to interact non-verbally. The group was hesitant when I first introduced guitars for them to play. "We're not musicians" they argued as they began to strum. Each guitar had been tuned to either a I, IV, or V chord. The participants became 'instant musicians' as I directed them. Later I introduced the use of the slide, allowing one guitar to play the I,IV,and V chords. For the tone chimes, lyrics were highlighted indicating when the chime was to ring. The melody was sung while the chimes provided a chordal accompaniment. All of these activities were designed for the immediate successful performance of a piece or composition. With each success the group developed trust in me as a facilitator and in each other.

Improvisations with rhythm instruments facilitated listening and fostered an increased awareness of nonverbal communication. The group found that rhythm elicited energy. In fact, they found this to be so invigorating that they would take instruments before the group and start their own improvisations. Sometimes this was a coping mechanism to bypass important issues. As the facilitator, I found it necessary to channel this energy towards the underlying needs of the group. Slowly the group began to recognize these behaviors which furthered personal growth and self awareness.

Songs were often used to initiate discussion. Members often revealed times when they had closed themselves off. After singing Simon and Garfunkel's 'I Am a Rock' they began to talk about how they would deflect their emotions, feeling as the song states, 'I am a rock, I am an island. And a rock feels no pain and an island never cries'. Discussions from these moments developed trust and intimacy. Members became more comfortable sharing and exploring emotions and the consequent behaviors that resulted.

Physical awareness was included in our goal of self awareness. In the group, deep breathing, stretching and progressive relaxation exercises, along with music helped the nurses to become more acquainted with their bodies. They learned to recognize tension and muscle stiffness and to practice techniques to alleviate these. This is one area that group members found most helpful. They expressed appreciation for the opportunity to take care of and practise self-motivation and care.

Through the use of visualization and music, nurses created and designed their own safe place. This sanctuary was free from life's stresses and personal problems. It was a peaceful place members could access anytime to rejuvenate their sense of well-being. Here nurses discovered inner strength, the beauty of self and the importance of self-healing. This state of awareness allowed inner peace and a new level of spirituality.

The goal of the hospice administration was to promote a sense of team. Before team building can begin, however, trust and communication must be present . To develop these the team was invited to participate in off-site days facilitated by the music therapist. These days were designed for personal renewal and revitalization. The team was divided into three groups to assure coverage of the patients and a manageable group size for the therapist.

Music focused the members, set the mood, created the atmosphere, directed the energy, and allowed for ventilation of feelings. While listening to music, staff members molded clay, painted, created collages or masks. Musical games helped clarify values, identify leaders, identify those who changed rules and those who would not allow the rules to be broken. Playing with a parachute to rhythm demanded that team members work together. Singing united the group and provided group acceptance. Relaxation exercises ended the day.

Staff support comes in many forms. Christmas parties, pool parties, and special recognition banquets all lend support. A 'pot-luck' on the fifth Tuesday of the month is assurance of our team gathering. In the Kaiser Permanente organization, the five Southern California Hospices also participate in a yearly retreat. The weekend is divided into accredited workshops, free time, and structured play time.

Providing staff support has been a challenge. I have become more aware of the burden of grief and loss especially while providing support to other departments outside of hospice. For hospice employees, even secretaries, grief and loss must be continually dealt with and expressed. I have come to understand that these feelings are always present and that music readily unleashes them. Even whimsical, silly, children's songs have reduced group members to tears.

I have found home care nurses to be special. They are empathetic, creative, and flexible. They have developed a keen sense of intuition that enables them to recognize patient needs. When music therapy began, I found this group of nurses extremely poor at recognizing and articulating their own needs. Also, they did not display to each other the same level of compassion that they showered their patients. Having recognized this, a commitment to supporting each other was made. Attitudes changed as nurses took time to affirm another's actions by saying 'I like the way you handled that' or 'You did a good job'. Within the group was a safe place to practice this or to confront another member. It was acceptable to ask 'Are you OK?' or 'What's going on with you?'

I knew that music therapy as staff support had made a difference but did not realize the extent to which it would positively effect hospice patients. The intimacy that had developed was evident to patients during visits made in collaboration with group members. Patients sensed the energy and commitment to their care. They relaxed immediately. Music allowed them to interact more freely and express themselves with the nurse in whom they had already placed much trust. Both patients and nurses recognized the depth of communication and acceptance present in the music.

Music therapy is an effective intervention for staff support. Music, in conjunction with the sensitivity of the therapist, provides a structure where feelings can be released while camaraderie and intimacy develops. Staff members can renew their commitment to palliative care.

Part Two

Techniques and Approaches

Songs Written by Palliative Care Patients in Music Therapy

Clare O'Callaghan
Kew, Australia

Introduction

Songwriting is a technique used by various music therapists working in palliative care including Bailey/Magill-Levreault,[19,11] Lane[8] and Salmon.[17] Salmon[17] recently described how songwriting was able to facilitate a couples' shared feelings with regard to one of the partner's illness. Magill-Levreault wrote: 'Composing music...to the words of the patient and family...helps to portray (their) feelings, images, dreams and fantasies.'[17] Lane also described songs written by cancer patients as gifts that can create a lasting musical memory.[8]

My first experience of songwriting in palliative care came through sessions with patients living with advanced multiple sclerosis who were quadriplegic, visually impaired and had moderate to severe cognitive impairment. Opportunities for them to express themselves creatively had dwindled alongside their physical and cognitive deterioration. The therapeutic potential of songwriting for these and other patients experiencing multiple sclerosis, other degenerative neurological conditions and cancer,[14] soon became obvious.

The purpose of this paper is to describe my songwriting work in palliative care. It will commence with a review of songwriting in use by music therapists in other health care settings.

Songwriting in Music Therapy

The initial descriptions of songwriting in music therapy[3] presented experiences with emotionally disturbed children, who spontaneously composed an opera, as well as songs about their family members. Later, composition as a psychotherapeutic approach with psychiatric patients was described by Rupenthal[16] and Castellano.[4] Ruppenthal[16] reported that the technique could facilitate tension release and guide patients to higher levels of social organisation and adjustment. Castellano[4] found that composition helped patients gain self-esteem and reinforced reality testing.

When describing songwriting with psychiatric, alcoholic and adolescent patients, Ficken[6] stated that it was 'an activity which can be internalised by the client leading to socially accepted behaviours'.[6] Freed[7] reported that songwriting allowed patients dependent on chemicals to feel supported and have their feelings validated, promoting an increase in self-esteem. Freed[7] also highlighted the importance of therapist's awareness of patients' symbolic use of metaphors.

Songwriting can facilitate repressed feelings,[6,12] strong feelings and opinions,[18] enhance insight into personal issues,[12] and provide opportunity for assessment[6,7]. Bruscia[2] regards songwriting (and song improvisation) as an important tool for the client or therapist to express the feeling of the moment verbally.

Much of the literature about songwriting in music therapy is placed within the context of groupwork.[18,12,15,7,3] Some of the advantages of groupwork are that patients can make suggestions for presented problems[7] and explore ways of integrating new found insights, behaviours or skills outside the group.[15] Edgerton[5] remarked that group song writing is especially effective in developing group cohesion, increasing self-esteem, providing an outlet for self-expression and encouraging a sense of belonging, participation, cooperation and pride.

Defining the Process

On reviewing a variety of songwriting articles, Edgerton[5] remarked that there is no universal way to approach composition in music therapy. She stated that lyric writing is the most frequently emphasised component and that composition is of only peripheral importance.

Whilst keeping the need to vary the structure in sessions according to clients' needs,[18] there are broad similarities amongst authors who have detailed their songwriting paradigms.[6,12,18,15,7,5] Four of six approaches present 'lead-in' or 'preparatory activities'[6,5,18,7] such as 'fill-in-the-gap' word substitution, or the analysis of pre-existing songs. All therapists except Plach[15] and Freed[7] encouraged lyric writing, and most followed with composition.

It is interesting to consider recent song developments, i.e. 'improvised song'[1] and 'improvising songs'.[3] Amir[1] described this process as a song '...produced in the moment according to the life force of the patient with the guidance of a music therapist and existing as a whole'. Wheeler[3] described it as a natural outgrowth of the process. The client could improvise songs at the end of a session and record them for later listening.

Context

There are many ways in which music therapists can encourage people to create songs. The clinical work and subsequent conclusions evolved from my work with 39 inpatients who wrote 64 songs over a period of about six-and-a-half years.[13] The patients were diagnosed with cancer or advanced neurological illnesses, mainly multiple sclerosis. Their ages ranged from 26 to over 80. Forty-three songs were written in individual sessions. Songs written by each patient spanned from one in a single session to eleven written over two years. Twenty-one songs were written by two or a group of patients. Within the the group sessions the number of songs ranged from one in a single session to eight songs spanning over 18 months. Most of the group sessions were with neurological patients.

Two thirds (26) of the patients had neurological conditions/problems and nine of these had moderate to severe cognitive impairment. Except for two, all of these were confined to wheelchairs or bed, with paraplegia or quadriplegia, weakness and dysarthria. Two patients were anarthric. One patient with motor neurone disease wrote the lyrics of his songs using head movements upon a microswitch attached to a specially designed computer. He communicated the musical accompaniment via an ETRAN Board (a perspex board that relies on the patients' eye movements for communication). Two neurological patients wrote some of their lyrics before arriving at music therapy, one manually, the other committing to memory, a staff member writing them out. One was mildly cognitively impaired, the other severely. One third (13) of the patients had advanced cancer. Most of these were weak and all allowed me to transcribe their lyrics for them. All except two patients appeared comfortable in terms of physical symptom control.

The individual sessions were held either in my room or at the patients' bedsides, in single or multi-bed wards. All of the group sessions were conducted in the patients' rooms which consisted of three or four bedded wards. Patients who resided in those rooms, and other selected patients, were invited to attend the sessions. The criteria for attending the neurological music therapy groups were that:

- the patients experienced similar types of cognitive impairment and cognitive abilities

- the patients did not attend other therapy or receive nursing attention at the time

- the patients' personality traits (which may be affected by brain-impairment) were comparable with other group members.

A song written by two cancer patients spontaneously arose from a group session in their room.

Within the sessions songwriting was only one of various music therapy techniques. Songwriting tended to be offered when patients expressed deep emotion, to enable validation and further ventilation of their feelings. It was also offered as a means to encourage achievement and pride, to enable significant expression of people important to them, and as a commentary about or celebration of a significant event. It was also used to encourage cohesion and support amongst the group members.

✗ Songwriting

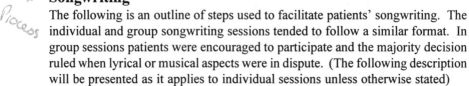

The following is an outline of steps used to facilitate patients' songwriting. The individual and group songwriting sessions tended to follow a similar format. In group sessions patients were encouraged to participate and the majority decision ruled when lyrical or musical aspects were in dispute. (The following description will be presented as it applies to individual sessions unless otherwise stated)

1. *Offer songwriting.* I offered songwriting to the patient if it was deemed appropriate. (Some patients initiated the songwriting after watching my work)
2. *Topic.* I either suggested a specific topic related to the session or offered a variety of topics reflecting different moods.

3. *Brainstorm.* If the patient agreed to songwriting and chose a theme, I encouraged him/her to brainstorm the chosen topic. If I needed to encourage I would ask specific questions or specific details, e.g. (topic: message to sons from 28 year old cancer patient) What would you like to say to T and J? Tell me what is special about T and J. What do you wish for their future?

Cognitively impaired patients normally required more structure. I found they responded best when encouraged to think concretely rather than abstractly and when offered questions that required yes or no answers, e.g. (a group of moderate to severe cognitively impaired patients were writing a song about staff members) Who would you like to include in your song, the nurses?

(answer: yes) Tell me what you think about the nurses, are thy kind?...there when you need them?..... Would you like to include the doctors? If a patient was severely impaired and unable to contribute a lengthy lyric I gave him/ her an opportunity to fill in a word at the end of a line by selecting from a choice of two words. If there was still no response I then said what about ...... and awaited the yes or no answer.

[Patients used the word-substitution technique for eleven songs. This involved the setting of new lyrics to an already known melody. The well known melody seemed to give the patients impetus to create their lyrics.]

4. ***Ideas Grouped into Related Themes.*** The ideas that emerged were grouped into related areas, usually by me (except where the patient wrote the complete lyrics). Often the patient was asked to identify the most important topics and these were put into a chorus with the patient's agreement. Other topics were then put into verses. Some patients chose through-composed styles (i.e. a series of verses).

5. ***Key.*** Melodic elements and the choice of major or minor keys were offered.

6. ***Rhythm.*** The rhythm tended to follow the natural rhythm of the speaking voice.

7. ***Mood.*** Preferred moods were ascertained as I improvised various musical styles. For example, a patient writing a liturgical piece requested that the piece be in Baroque style. I offered a choice between slow moving melodies with chordal accompaniment and quicker, syncopated melodies with a running, broken chord accompaniment.

8. ***Melody.*** The patient was invited to suggest melodies for each line. I usually gave a choice of two melodic fragments. I tended to offer one choice that was an exaggeration of the natural melodic intonation my speaking voice, should I have spoken the lyrics.

9. ***Accompaniment, Dynamics, Tempo, Instrumentation and Voicing.*** Interested patients (only a few) chose the style of accompaniment, dynamics, tempo, instrumentation and voicing. I selected the harmonies that centred on the I, II, IV, V and VI chords, with numerous major and minor sevenths and passing notes to add interest. Most of the melodies that were longer than four lines also included a modulation to a related key.

35

10. *Title.* The patient normally named the song.

11. *Write-Up, Record.* I wrote out the song and either the patient or I recorded it (usually I did this). On one occasion the patient's brother recorded her song in a recording studio after the patient's death.

Most of the songs, especially those written by individuals, took one complete session. Some of the group songs and the songs composed by an anarthric, quadriplegic patient took numerous sessions.

Reflections

The structure in songwriting sessions, i.e. how involved I became in assisting patients to make choices, was determined by the patients' cognitive functioning and energy levels. My aim was to provide enough structure for patients to both compose and possess the songs as their own. Many patients were proud of their achievements and on occasions would present them to listeners.

An important conclusion of this work was that patients with severe cognitive and/or physical impairments could create songs. To illustrate this I will describe the songwriting contribution of a patient with Steele Richardon's Syndrome [a rapidly progressive Parkinson's like condition]. This anarthric patient was described as having dementia and communicated by raising one finger for 'yes' and two fingers for 'no'. She often held the deciding vote for the group on which melody was to be selected for each lyrical line. When the group responded favourably to her choices her face moved slightly, (into her 'smile', she uttered a grunting laugh and rocked).

The patients' songs included liturgical pieces for performance at the hospital's ecumenical services and a love song that I sang at the composer's wedding. Others included songs for spouses, children and grandchildren which expressed the meaning that they had in the patients' lives. One song was written to celebrate the patient and his wife's golden wedding anniversary. Another patient composed a lullaby for a grandchild born in England. She also learnt the autoharp and accompanied herself singing the lullaby which was recorded and sent to her new grandson. Patients also wrote songs to celebrate special events, such as the hospital acquiring a home brew kit. Many songs were tributes to staff. Some were written to staff leaving the hospital and two were for a memorial services following the deaths of a patient and a staff member. Patients used many songs to express tributes to each other and to patients who had died. Many songs included prayers to God and others included thoughts about special places, both from their memories and fantasies. Some also wrote about their illness. One called her song, which expressed her struggles living with lymphoma for over ten years, 'The Holocaust'.

Research

Using modified grounded theory and content analysis research approaches I systematically analysed the lyrics of the 64 songs written by 39 palliative care patients in palliative care music therapy sessions. Patients used most songs (87%) as a means of expressing important messages. In two thirds of the songs patients reflected upon aspects about themselves; in half patients expressed compliments to other people; and almost half of the songs (45%) included memories. Other recurring themes included reflections upon patients' significant others (31%), self-expression of adversity (25%), imagery (17%) and prayers (11%). It was argued that the emerging themes indicated that song writing could alleviate some of the physical, social, emotional and spiritual needs of palliative care patients.[13]

As the research was retrospective I was unable to explore the systematic effects of the songwriting process on the lives of patients and those for whom they were written. Many patients were proud of their songs, informing others of their achievements and presenting the music, either live or on taped, to those close to them. The positive messages that patients wrote to each other in their songs affirmed feelings of self-worth. Some patients found it easier to express their thoughts through lyrics than words. One sister of a patient came to me with tears and said that it was the only time that her sister had ever said thank you for keeping her out of an institution for so long. The songs often helped the patients' lovers and families in their bereavement. One mother said that listening to her son's recording of her daughter's song eased some of the pain relating to the daughter's death. Further evidence that these songs may help was given when a another mother requested that I play one of her son's compositions at his funeral.

Conclusion

Although songwriting in palliative care is a relatively new discipline, the connection between death, dying and music extends to antiquity.[10] Song creation has assisted many people, from numerous cultures, to work through their grief during bereavement. Music therapists have the opportunity to enable palliative care patients to work through many thoughts and feelings, through song writing. A precedent for the use of composition to ease the journey toward death can be found amongst the American Indians. Around adolescence, the Indians each found their own death chant via, for example, a vision or a dream.[9] This centring technique helped them cope with adversity, enabling them to feel that they had a path to follow to the 'Great Spirit' each moment until their death (ibid. pp. 25-

37

26). Song writing may enhance palliative care patients' (and their significant others') abilities to cope with their dying, and it may also enhance the quality of their living. As Levine wrote: "Whatever prepares you for death enhances life."[9]

References

1. Amir D (1990). A song is born: discovering meaning in improvised songs through a phenomenological analysis of two music therapy sessions with a traumatic spinal-cord injured young patient. *Music Therapy*; *9(1)*: 62-81.

2. Bruscia KE (1988). Songs in Psychotherapy. Paper presented at the 14th Australian Music Therapy Association Conference, Melbourne.

3. . Bruscia KE (1987). *Improvisational Models of Music Therapy*, Springfield: Charles C. Thomas.

4. Castellano JA (1969). Music composition in a music therapy program. *Journal of Music Therapy*; *6*: 12-14.

5. Edgerton CD (1990). Creative group song writing. *Music Therapy Perspectives*; *8*: 15-19.

6. Ficken T (1976). The use of song writing in a psychiatric setting. *Journal of Music Therapy*; *13(4)*: 163-172.

7. Freed B (1987). Song writing with the chemically dependent. *Music Therapy Perspectives*; *4*: 13-18.

8. Lane D (1992). Music therapy: a gift beyond measure. *Oncology Nursing Forum*; *19(6)*: 863-867.

9. Levine S (1982). *Who Dies: An Investigation into Conscious Living and Conscious Dying*. NY: Anchor Books.

10. Lloyd AL (1980). Lament. In: Sadie S (Ed), *The New Grove Dictionary of Music and Musicians* (Vol 10, pp. 407-410). London: MacMillan Pub.

11. Magill-Levreault L (1993). Music therapy in pain and symptom management. *Journal of Palliative Care*; *9(4)*: 42-48.

12. Murphy M (1983). Music therapy: a self-help group for substance abuse patients. *Music Therapy*; *3(1)*: 52-62.

13. O'Callaghan C (1994). Song Writing in Palliative Care. MMus Thesis, University of Melbourne.

14. O'Callaghan C (1990). Music therapy skills used in song writing within a palliative care setting. *Australian Journal of Music Therapy*; *1*: 15-22.

15. Plach T (1980). *The Creative Use of Music in Group Therapy*. Springfield: Charles C. Thomas.

16. Rupenthal W (1965). 'Scribbling' in music therapy. *Journal of Music Therapy*; *2*: 8-9.

17. Salmon D (1993). Music and emotion in palliative care. *Journal of Palliative Care*; *9(4)*: 48-52.

18. Schmidt JA (1983). Song writing as a therapeutic process. *Music Therapy Perspectives*; *1(2)*: 4-7.

19. Slivka HH & Bailey LM (1986). The conjoint use of social work and music therapy with children of cancer patients. *Music Therapy*; *6A(1)*: 30-40.

Access To Music In
Pediatric Bereavement Support Groups

Katherine L Ryan
Cleveland, USA

Hospice of the Western Reserve Mission

The Hospice believes that everyone has a right to appropriate medical care. Hospice services are provided by a specially trained team of professionals and volunteers. The team includes physicians, nurses, home nursing assistants, social workers, bereavement coordinators, music therapists, art therapists, spiritual care coordinators, volunteers and others who work within the community. Hospice care supports the patient and family to help live as fully as possible, and continues assistance through the bereavement period. Our services are available regardless of ability to pay.

The population served is urban and suburban, therefore, patients represent many religious, cultural and socio-economic backgrounds. Patients are seen where they are, in their private home, nursing facility, or group living environment. Patient ages range from newborns to 95+ years, their principle diagnoses include cancer, heart disease, lung disease, neurological disease, AIDS, Alzheimer's disease, and other various terminal illnesses. In 1993 there were 1,498 new patients and 1,733 total patients served.

Music and art therapists work within this hospice framework under the discipline of Expressive Therapy. Hospice of the Western Reserve recognizes the value of the arts in hospice care and is dedicated to providing to patients and their families the opportunity for expression through music and art. Music therapy has been a significant part of the services of Hospice of the Western Reserve since 1986 when the first part-time music therapist was added to the staff. The program expanded to a full-time music therapist in 1989. Two years later a second full-time music therapist was added due to an increased patient census and an associated increase in requests for music therapy services. With the addition of an art therapist in 1994 the program has expanded its services. The following is a description of the Expressive Therapy program:

41

What is Expressive Therapies in Hospice?

As a vital part of the hospice interdisciplinary team, the expressive therapies offer hospice patients and their families opportunities to focus on the creative process as a means of expression, communication, relaxation, stimulation, pain relief/distraction and connection. In hospice, the expressive therapies represent a holistic approach, or one in which the patient or family member is addressed mentally, physically, emotionally and spiritually.

Underneath the expressive therapies umbrella, the use of music and art interventions create a structure in which verbal and non-verbal interaction enhance the quality of the life. Expressive therapists use the tools and methods of the arts to help patients and family members understand and express themselves.

The process involves much more than encouraging or assisting a patient in producing some art form. The entire process, from choice of medium to method, style and creation of a finished product involves expression.

Commencing in 1992, the Hospice embarked on the formal development of pediatric bereavement support groups offered to any child that has suffered a loss of a loved one. Hospice had offered adult support groups to the bereaved for years and as family members and other agencies asked for similar support for children, the agency looked to refer to other support entities. However, it was discovered that the availability of support services were limited and inconsistent. Hospice of the Western Reserve began a specialized Pediatric Team in 1992 to care for families and their seriously ill children. At that time, the team requested that children's support groups be offered by staff who had experience in working with children who had experienced loss. The challenge proposed in creating this program was to offer groups for children that were structured, yet creative, and would give children the opportunity to express in ways that would permit them to feel comfortable. As the pediatric bereavement support groups were developed, the pediatric social worker and music therapist, who co-facilitated the groups, consulted with pediatric team members. Needs brought to discussion included, but were not limited to, providing a place for children suffering from loss to come together, providing a safe environment, facilitating the childrens' understanding of feelings and offering a supportive environment where they can form new relationships with others who may be having similar experiences. The following general purpose and goals were established for the pediatric bereavement support groups:

Purpose: To provide bereaved children a safe place to identify, express and become more comfortable with the many aspects of their grief.

Goal: To give children tools to cope with grief and assist them in expressing and normalizing feelings within a group setting.

As details of the program were being finalized, it was decided to integrate the arts as a part of each group. Staff experience and the literature supported the concept that the children naturally use the arts as their first modes of expression. McIntyre and Raymer[1] identified that: 'the arts become primary tools in facilitating the expression and resolution of grief, especially (although not exclusively) in children and adolescents'.

Each support group is a closed group for children ages 8-12. It meets weekly for a six week period. This time frame allows for relationships to build and support work to be accomplished. The six week group series is offered for any child that has experienced the loss of a loved one. Parents/guardians and the children are requested to be at the group at a specified time in the early evening. At that time refreshments are served and the group may socialize for 30 minutes. The children's support group then begins and lasts for one hour. Some groups have been fortunate to have parents/guardians become a part of a separate informal support atmosphere, where discussion may revolve around the parent's/guardian's grief and that of their children. In those instances, a Hospice Bereavement Coordinator has assisted.

The six sessions consist of weekly themes which provide a basis for intervention planning. The themes are as follows:

- Tell Your Story
- Exploring Grief: Externally and Internally
- Alternative Modes of Expression
- Memory Exploration
- Changes In The Family
- Future- How to Say Good-bye

The support group format was established to incorporate three elements in each group experience; music therapy, the talking stick tradition, and various arts activities (drama, art, writing, poetry, etc.). Each segment was designed to provide flexibility in the extent of structure developed in the group for the group to be more or less structured, depending on the individual and group personalities.

The group structure flows clockwise around a circle (Figure 1) with suggested time and interventions.

The group format presents the philosophy of transmodal group membership. Each letter represents a group member's level of involvement in an intervention, single group session or the entire six week program. For instance child A may be very active in every activity, ready to express, eager to talk and share. Child A may change modes by spiraling inward as represented by child D who observes others, receives our encouragement and reinforcement, but chooses not to share, acting as a sponge absorbing what is happening in the room. Child B and child C may stay in their present mode throughout an activity, group session or the entire six week program, however, the flexibility is there for the group member to change their involvement level at any time. Each group member always has the option to 'pass' if asked to share . The focus then for the facilitators is to be aware that each group member is present and is hearing and interacting on different levels.

Group Structure - *Figure 1*

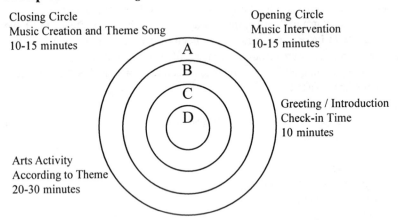

Closing Circle
Music Creation and Theme Song
10-15 minutes

Opening Circle
Music Intervention
10-15 minutes

Greeting / Introduction
Check-in Time
10 minutes

Arts Activity
According to Theme
20-30 minutes

Example A	Very active	Example D	Observes others
			Receives encouragement
Example B	Active		Receives reinforcement
	Needs encouragement		Chooses not to share
Example C	Observes others		
	Needs encouragement		
	Needs positive reinforcement		

For each session the interventions and activities planned relate to themes, issues and feelings raised during the previous session. The facilitators (music therapist and social worker) attempt to assist in the development of each intervention and activity in a manner that provides a rational and comfortable transition. If the intervention or activity presents difficulty for a group member the facilitators may attempt to discuss the child's success in the music intervention with which the group began. It may then be possible for the child to proceed to the current task, complete it, and resume the session. The music intervention can become a grounding, positive experience for the group members. Plach[2] identified four advantages of using music in group work. He states that the music holds the ability to evoke and identify feelings, provides a vehicle for expression, stimulates verbalizations and provides a reliable starting and ending place. The facilitators of the pediatric bereavement support groups have focused on these advantages as well as using music therapy interventions as a means of expression and as an avenue to encourage verbal expression. In planning music interventions it is very important for the music therapist to be clear about how and why a specific intervention is being used. The following checklist adapted from the work of McIntyre and Raymer[1] may assist with choosing appropriate music interventions and focusing on the role of music in facilitating grief.

Role of Music in Facilitating Grief
Adapted from B McIntyre and M Raymer

Affirmation
- music promotes affirmation of life when faced with loss
- music can be created which affirms life and confers meaning

Control
- music offers child choices to obtain control over self and his/her situation
- music offers the child a sense of control over a powerless situation

Uniqueness
- music can assist child to discover and affirm his/her uniqueness
- music can be created by the child that promotes ownership

Remembrance
- music evokes memories
- music promotes commemoration of a loved one who died
- music promotes creation of new memories

P.T.O.

Awareness
- music promotes awareness of here and now
- music promotes awareness of others
- music promotes awareness of interactions with friends/strangers
- music promotes awareness of building new relationships

The role of music in facilitating grief is very important when planning music therapy interventions. In this sense planning consists of both initial and continuous planning that takes place after debriefing of each group session. Plach[2] also developed eight guidelines for group therapy which have been adapted for the pediatric bereavement support group framework. The following guidelines have been helpful in music intervention planning for the grief support groups to date.

General Guidelines for Music Intervention Planning
Adapted from T Plach

1. The appropriate music intervention should adhere to the individual and group needs, which may be affected by individual group member's death experiences, and should be within the conceptual, integrative, or social limitations that exist within the group.

2. Music chosen for any music intervention should take into consideration cultural and age factors that exist within the group.

3. The music interventions chosen need to be flexible in order to vary the nature and extent of structure needed to facilitate successful individual and group interactions and make the intervention successful.

4. The nature and level of participation by the facilitators in the music intervention should be directly related to and determined by the needs of the group members and the maximization of their experience of the intervention.

5. All individual and group responses to an intervention are valid.

6. De-brief individual and group responses to the session with facilitators immediately after each group session to maximize planning and implementing individual and group needs for the next session.

7. Whenever appropriate, refer back to the initial music intervention including

individual and group responses to that intervention. This practice can re-direct and assist group members with individual reactions and emotions. It can also enable focusing on activities and behaviors which facilitate reconciliation.

8. Whenever appropriate, encourage group members to use music intervention skills that they are learning outside of the group. If they have had experiences doing this during the six week series and they are comfortable, encourage them to share these experiences with the group.

The facilitators have found that each of these guidelines have been crucial in planning due to the diverse population of group members, death experiences, and grief processes.

In experience to date, the music therapist and social worker have confronted several challenges in their work and the format they have chosen. The need for continuous evaluation of the program has become very important. The final support group meeting includes having the group members fill out an evaluation form and draw a picture about their support group experience. This has been helpful in evaluating activities, interventions and the group process. The evaluation process is also extended to parents/guardians in a different format to inquire about their perceptions of the support group and what changes they may or may not have seen in their child/children. Evaluations have been helpful in the continuous development of the program and in educating and explaining group responses to various staff members.

Through internal evaluation it was determined that the program needed to be introduced to the community and those who needed the services. Therefore, an extensive mailing was sent to targeted agencies and individuals who may be interested in our support groups, either for themselves or their clients. A brochure containing information about the time, place and content of our groups was sent to health and human service agencies within our service area. Examples of these would include counseling agencies, children's hospitals and funeral homes. Individualized cover letters accompanied the brochures that were sent to hospice families that had children who may be appropriate for the group. This included families who had lost a child and still had children in the home or where a child had lost a significant adult. Letters and brochures were also sent to the facilitators of other support groups in the area that worked with parents who had lost a child. Because these adults were participating in a group for themselves, we hoped they would want their surviving children to benefit from a group experience also. School systems were also contacted so that school counselors would be informed about our groups and be able to refer appropriate children. In addition, school based support groups and staff inservices were offered.

At the time of this writing the pediatric bereavement support group program has been clinically implemented for approximately 18 months. In its initial stages there were intermittent developmental problems which were primarily related to dissemination of information to the community. In the last year, knowledge of the program and staff familiarity with the process has assisted in presenting the services quite successfully. Evaluation responses, although not formally tabulated or reported, indicate a high rate of group member and parent/guardian approval and satisfaction with the program. Experience indicates that the pediatric bereavement support group program is one for which there is a specific and real need, that the need for the series will continue.

Music Therapy Interventions

The following music therapy interventions have been created or adapted for use during the opening circle of the group format. Each intervention has been successful in group thus far and can be modified to address the needs of the group members. Each example provides the purpose of the intervention, the materials required and a brief description.

Intervention Example 1
Introduction of the Theme Song

Purpose: To establish a ritual in providing a common ending place for the group session.
To provide affirmation of the group experience.
To provide acknowledgment of relationships.

Materials required: accompanying instrument

The theme song is a piece that is used in closing each group session during the six week series. It establishes a familiar activity as the children bring closure to each group session. The song is usually introduced by the therapist while a group member assists in playing the accompaniment. The children can learn the song line by line. It is usually sung as many times as there are group members so that each child has the opportunity to play the accompanying instrument. A different instrument can be used for each session, the song remaining the familiar element. The Suzuki Omnichord is popular due to fact that the children can

48

initiate, choose and control rhythm patterns. Some members choose not to play as the instrument is passed throughout the circle. The 'pass' option is always given to group members. The style in which the song is sung can also vary and be the choice of the person accompanying the group. The music styles have varied from country to the hard rock. The option of support groups creating their own theme song should also be considered. Lyrics to original songs are always included in the memory folders.

Theme song example:
(see figure 2)   Can you hear the song we sing?
Can you see the friendship we bring?
With our voices we can share,
Knowing the people we talk to will care!

                            Written by Katherine Ryan, RMT-BC

Intervention Example 2
Lay Some Happiness On Me

Purpose: To promote socialization and relationship building via group interaction and cooperation.
To promote awareness of interaction with others.
To promote an avenue of verbal expression through identification of feelings in the lyrics of the song.

Materials required: none

This song enhances interaction and may assist group members to break the social barriers that may be created when coming together. After teaching the song, the therapist and a group member can demonstrate clapping each others hands on the last two beats of each line. This can be in groups of two, however, when seated in a circular formation the group can extend their hands to their sides and clap hands with each person seated next to them. The group members may become more aware of themselves and others through clapping their hands. Discussion about various feelings that the lyrics acknowledge and the experience of sharing physical and spatial awareness may result.

Figure 2

Can You Hear the Song We Sing?

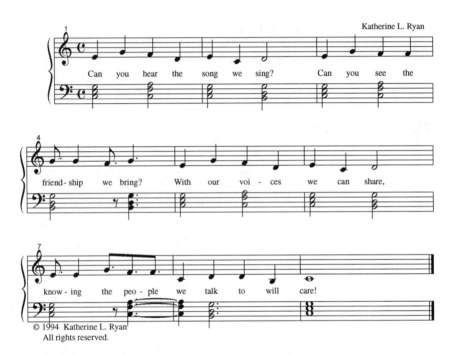

Intervention Example 3
Rhythm Instrument Exploration

Purpose: To create sounds that identify feelings, affirm and confer meaning.
To develop a sense of choice and control through creativity.
To provide a means of non-verbal communication.

Materials required: Rhythm instruments (as many as there people in the
group) that vary in texture, color, sound and how they are played.

Rhythm instruments are placed within the circle so that each child can see them. Members are asked to look at each of the instruments and decide which instrument sound represents how they are feeling or have felt at some point during the past week. The therapist may need to demonstrate how each instrument is played and how it sounds. Group members then take turns picking their instrument, playing it, and if comfortable, sharing the feeling the sound represented. The instrument is placed within the circle and the next group member may begin. Following the activity, discussion may revolve around the various sounds and feelings played, always respecting each person's unique interpretations, feelings and choices.

Intervention Example 4
"This is a Song About..."
Taught at the University of Texas Medical Branch Galveston, Texas

Purpose: To identify what makes group members unique.
To promote creating music.
To promote relationship building through identifying who the
grieving person is.

Materials required: accompanying instrument and voices

Explain to group members that they will be involved in creating a song through asking and answering various questions. The therapist sings a question to a group member. During the member's turn he/she answers the question. As they answer the group can assist by singing the various questions and responses with the therapist or after learning the initial song can create new questions for the song.

Figure 3

This is a Song About...

From the University of Texas Medical Branch
Galveston, Texas

Example: *(see figure 3)*

> This is a song about ___(Katie)_____.
> Her favorite color is ____(Blue)_____.
> Her favorite food is __(Pizza)_____.
> Her favorite TV show is __(Superman)___.
> __(Katie)__ likes to ___(sing)__.
> But doesn't like to ___(clean)___.
> This is a song about ____(Katie)__.
> Let's all say hello!

Intervention Example 5
Drum Improvisation

Purpose: To provide a means of non-verbal communication.
To provide less-verbal group members with an activity in which they can participate more fully.
To encourage imagination in self-expression.

Materials required: various sizes of wood frame hand drums

The drums are placed in the circle and attention is brought to the various sizes and the different quality of sounds. Examples of how sounds can be produced on the drum can be given as well. This experience offers group members the opportunity to improvise feelings on the drums. Many approaches can be taken depending on group needs and interactions. This exercise may be accomplished on an individual basis as with the rhythm instrument intervention. It can also be expanded with the following ideas:

- In groups of two, one person improvises an identified feeling on the drum and the partner tries to guess what the feeling may be.

- As a group, one person improvises an identified feeling with the drum and the group guesses what the feeling may be.

- Incorporate drumming into musical charades where one person is improvising a feeling as the group guesses what the feeling may be.

- Move from individual sounds on the drums (with or without verbal explanations) to a group sound.

- Have one group member begin with a sound on their drum and have others move in with their sounds one by one to establish a group sound; the group could then continue with fading out sounds the same way they came in. This could lead to discussion about depending on each other and how community changes when one or two sounds are no longer present.

- General drum improvisation

Intervention Example 6
Imagine

Purpose: To promote a mode of communication through song writing.
To create an awareness of wishful thinking as opposed to the here and now.
To create a form of remembrance of the group experience.

Materials required: outline of song, accompanying instrument, writing utensils

This activity takes a song that may be familiar to some children and recreates it to communicate the groups thoughts. This can be done individually, however, the group problem solving experience in deciding what they want to communicate is an interesting process. The group fills in the outlined structure paying some attention to the number of syllables needed (flexibility is very important). The group can hear the song in full and decide if there are any changes that need to be made. The song can be recorded in its final form and played on the last day for parents. Words to songs are always written out and put into memory folders. Copies of the tape can be given if funds permit.

IMAGINE by J Lennon

C	F	
IMAGINE THERE'S NO		(2 SYLLABLES)
C	F	
IT'S	IF YOU TRY	(HARD OR EASY)
C	F	
NO		(4 SYLLABLES)
C	F	
ONLY		(4 SYLLABLES)

Am			Dm			
IMAGINE_____						(4 SYLLABLES)

G			A7			
LIVING _____						(3 SYLLABLES)

F	G			C	E	
YOU MAY_____						(5 SYLLABLES)

F	G			C	E	
BUT I _____						(5 SYLLABLES)

F	G			C	E	
I HOPE _____						(5 SYLLABLES)

F	G			C		
AND THE WORLD						(4 SYLLABLES)

Arts Activities

The following arts activities (drama, art, writing, poetry, etc.) have been created or adapted for use during the arts activity portion of the group format. Each activity has been successful in group thus far and can be modified to address the needs of the group members. Each example provides the materials required and a brief description. Background music has been used during some of the arts activities. For some children it breaks the silence in the room, facilitates discussion and/or fosters an idea. Most of the background music chosen has been from popular tunes in rock music that incorporate a loss theme in the lyrics (i.e. Prayer for the Dying by Seal, I'll Be There by Mariah Carey, Tears in Heaven by Eric Clapton).

Memory Folders

Materials required: plain colored two-pocket folders, stickers, collage materials, crayons, markers, pens, pencils, glue.

Ask children to decorate a folder with art that reminds them of their deceased loved one. Explain that the folders will be filled with the handouts and creations that will be accumulated during the six-week series. Play soft, popular music in the background to enhance the experience. Music chosen can relate to themes of grief and/or loss. Children can choose to share their folders with the group at the end of the activity.

Aspects of Grief

Materials required: large poster board, markers.

This is a didactic activity utilizing discussion to explore the many different aspects of grief. Children sit in a circle while facilitators lead them in a discussion about the feelings they have about their loved one's death. One facilitator records these feelings on the poster board in order to make them tangible. Following the session, the aspects of grief compiled by the group are transferred to letter sized sheets of paper. Distribute the handouts to the children during the next session for inclusion in their memory folders.

Letters to a Significant Other

Materials required: papers, pens, pencils.

Review the many aspects of grief discussed during the last session. Ask them to write a letter to someone they trust relaying their grief experience. Discuss the benefits of sharing feelings with other people, noting that writing is one alternative to talking. Play soft, popular music in the background to enhance the experience. Music chosen can relate to themes of grief and/or loss. Children can choose to share their letters with the group at then end of the activity. The letters are then placed in their memory folders.

Feelings Charades

Materials required: Feeling cards- a set of index cards with a different feeling printed on each one, nylon scarf.

Distribute five to eight feelings cards to each child. Direct them to choose one feeling that is meaningful. This can be a feeling they have personally felt or have seen expressed by someone else. Children take turns acting out their feeling without using words while the group attempts to guess the correct feeling. The children use the scarf by holding it in front of their face as a curtain and then dropping it when they are ready to begin their charade. This activity can lead to discussion about alternate ways to express feelings.

Memory Objects

Materials needed: Polaroid camera, film.

During the previous session, children are asked to bring an object that reminds them of their deceased loved one. Children take turns sharing their objects. They explain the object, it's meaning and the memories it evokes. Each child is photographed with their memory object. The photograph is included in the memory folder by itself or attached to the child's cinquin.

Cinquins

Materials needed: pens, pencils, paper, glue, cinquin outline.

Facilitators explain the format of a five-line cinquin. Each child writes a cinquin poem that relates to their memory object. When the poem is completed, the memory object picture can be attached to the paper and placed into the memory folder.

Body Outlines

Materials needed: large roll of paper cut into body size lengths, markers, crayons, heart shaped note paper.

Children are divided into pairs. Each child lies down on their sheet of paper while their partner outlines their body. Children finish outline by drawing their clothes and features. Facilitators encourage children to identify people in their lives that love and support them as well as things they find pleasurable. Children put these names and activities on the heart shaped notes and glue them on or around their body outline. Soft, popular music can be played in the background to enhance the experience. Music chosen can relate to themes of grief and/or loss.

Letter to the Deceased

Materials needed: paper, pens, pencils.

Facilitators encourage children to discuss their feelings about their deceased loved one. Children compose a letter to the person that they lost. This often provides an opportunity for children to say good-bye to their loved one if they were not able to do that before. Soft, popular music can be played in the background to enhance the experience. Music chosen can relate to themes of grief and/or loss. This also ties into discussion regarding the conclusion of group and the need to say good-bye to the facilitators and other group members. The letter is added to the memory folders.

References

1. McIntyre B & Raymer M (1989). Expressive therapies in pediatric hospice care. *Pediatric hospice care: What helps* (pp 96 -115). Los Angeles: Children's Hospital of Los Angeles.

 2. Plach T (1980). *Creative use of music in group therapy*. Illinois: Charles Thomas Publishing.

Resource Bibliography

Books

Bowlby J (1980). *Loss: Sadness and depression*. Harper-Collins.

Osterweis M Soloman F & Green M (eds). (1984). *Bereavement: reactions, consequences and care.* Committee for the Study of Consequences of the Stress of Bereavement. Institute of Medicine. Washington D.C.: National Academy Press.

Rando T (1986). *Parental loss of a child*. Illinois: Research Press Company.

Schmitt B & Guzzino M (1985). Expressive therapy with children in crisis: A new avenue of communication. In: Corr C & Corr D (eds), *Hospice Approaches to Pediatric Care* (pp 155-177). New York: Springer Publishing Company.

Walsh F & McGoldrick M (1991). *Living beyond loss: Death in the family*. New York: WW Norton.

Periodical Literature

Anshel A & Kipper D (1988). The influence of group singing on trust and cooperation. *Journal of Music Therapy; 25:* 145-155.

Bartholome W (1993). Care for the dying child: The demands of ethics. *Second Opinion; 18*(4): 24-39.

Cassity M (1976). The influence of music therapy activity on peer acceptance, group cohesiveness and interpersonal relationships of adult psychiatric patients. *Journal of Music Therapy; 25:* 66-76.

Harvey A (1988). Human suffering and the therapeutic value of creative expression through music. *The Creative Child and Adult Quarterly; 8*: 10-16.

Kagin S & Lusebring V (1978). The Expressive Therapies Continuum. *Journal of Art Psychotherapy; 5*: 171-180.

McIntyre BB (1990). An art therapy group for bereaved youth in hospice care. *Caring; 8(9)*: 56-58.

McIntyre BB (1990). Art therapy with bereaved youth. *Journal of Palliative Care; 6(1)*: 16-25.

Norris-Shortle C, Young P & Williams M (1993). Understanding death and grief for children three and under. *Social Work; 38(6)*: 736-742.

Sontag M, Nadig J & Henry L (1994). The children's grief workshop: Social work practice in hospice. *The American Journal of Hospice and Palliative Care; 14(3)*: 23-29.

Stahl L (1990). Music therapy and the grieving child. *Thanatos; 15(3)*: 13-15.

Music Therapy with Patients Undergoing Radiation and Chemotherapy

Friederike von Hodenberg
Hamburg, Germany

As a member of a team of psychologists and sociologists, I am researching the use of music therapy with a group of patients undergoing radiation and chemotherapy in the University Clinic in Hamburg. The project had already been established for six months when I joined. Before this I had worked with children and their parents on a paediatric ward in the University Clinic. Clinical space was at a premium, therefore music therapy took place at the bedside. This paper will deal with the following topics:

- alleviation of pain through relaxation
- impact of rhythm and tone on breathing
- musical responses from severely withdrawn patients
- facilitation of emotional expression through music
- music and the consolidation of self-esteem

This writing is based around anecdotal experiences and summaries of methods used. It provides the background for the more specific areas to be dealt with in the research.

Florian

Florian, aged four, was admitted to the children's ward where he received chemotherapy. As I entered Florian's room his mother remarked on the fact that I had my Lyre. This, she explained, was a familiar instrument played by Florian's sister. I asked Florian if he recognised it. When he indicated 'yes', I realised that the Lyre might have represented the human element within the clinical world of medicine. This, I hoped, would allow for receptive music therapy.

Florian's mother asked him if I should play. He nodded; he was shy, fragile and very ill. I played softly in the pentatonic scale, observing his reactions. In my experience, the pentatonic scale produces a feeling of flowing and movement. Florian watched me carefully, sucking his dummy. These were signs that made me realise he accepted my playing. Eventually he fell asleep. Florian rarely spoke in our meetings, accepting the music, deciding for himself whether he wanted to be close to me or not. The music allowed a freedom in our relationship which may not have occurred through silence. Our communication was built through mutual understanding and acceptance.

During Florian's music therapy, the role of his mother was crucial. She was with him constantly providing security and love. Both were shy and sensitive and responded positively to the music. Her needs were as great as his. The vibrations created an atmosphere in which Florian could sleep. This also allowed his mother room to talk about her situation. She did not as yet feel able to discuss the implications of Florian's illness. I realised that two relationships were developing rather than one.

Agreement was reached that I would play the Lyre during sessions. Florian was given the opportunity to dictate the content of sessions through directing when the music began and ended. The structure of the music therapy hour was flexible. At times, Florian sucked his dummy rhythmically to the music, thus becoming an active participant in what was intrinsically receptive music therapy. I allowed Florian to respond by playing carefully chosen tones followed by silence. He would answer the musical phrases with his eyes, ultimately falling asleep. During sessions his mother would also relax. On the surface it would seem that she played only a passive role. Subsequent conversations revealed, however, that the music had focussed her attention on various situations in her life and enabled her to express them. This change from the non-verbal to the verbal again highlighted the potential for active receptivity. Each session created its own form that allowed for future development.

Florian's condition began to deteriorate. Regular chemotherapy sessions left him physically unable to take part in music therapy sessions. Even though the meetings were now irregular the relationship became more intense. The Lyre took on greater importance as an intermediary object in the relationship between Florian and myself. Also, the verbal explorations with his mother allowed greater trust in our relationship.

62

There came a crucial shift when the doctors informed his mother that Florian's condition had now become critical. He left hospital and moved back to his home. From now until his death I worked with Florian, his mother and other members of his family. Florian never allowed me to play the Lyre again. Whilst he never gave a reason for this decision, I believe that it might have reminded him of his time in hospital. Instead, I decided to tell him the story of 'The Little Prince'[1] Through the dialogue I offered Florian the opportunity to talk about his concepts of dying. It transpired that the important theme was of the Prince being in heaven. In the story, the Prince comes to earth to find friends. When he eventually finds them he returns to heaven. I began to realise that this story mirrored Florian's life and impending death. At one point in the story Florian remarked, *"I believe there are more 'little humans' in heaven than on earth."* His mother also told me that he once said, *"Mummy, Friederike has a wonderful voice when she tells the story of the Little Prince."* During his last days Florian only wanted to hear the beginning of the story. I repeated it at least ten times, concentrating on the tone-quality of my voice as a means to calm and relax him.

After his death I continued my relationship with his mother. We talked in great depth about the sessions and the power of communication between Florian, his mother and myself as music therapist. It is our intention to now write a book about our experiences.

Ann

Ann came to the clinic after a transplant. It was subsequently discovered that she had a tumour which needed to be treated with radiation. My first impression was of an open, kind lady who seemed interested in what music therapy might have to offer. During our first meeting, we discussed what music might be appropriate for her and which instrument would be best suited. We further discussed Ann's past musical experiences and the instruments that she had played. I asked for her views on using music as a means for spiritual support and the potential she had to reactivate her forgotten musical abilities. At the end of our first session we agreed that in future I would bring my Lyre.

At the beginning of the second session I placed my Lyre on Ann's bed. She initially tried to play but soon returned it to me and asked me to play. I began with a piece by JS Bach. The music had a clear form, allowing Ann to experience the construction and textures whilst keeping an emotional distance. After a short pause I continued with some modern-day popular songs. At first Ann listened, then hummed, and finally sang out loud. Through her singing a dialogue began. Ann listened to the tones, accepting the sound, humming and singing with the Lyre. This was the beginning of our relationship. Ann was astonished that she was able to sing, discovering a long lost voice. Afterwards she remembered familiar life situations when she had sung. The fact that she was able to sing even when she was so ill reinforced her self-confidence. At the end of the session, Ann asked me to sing for her. She relaxed and closed her eyes.

When I arrived for the third session Ann was sitting in her chair. She complained about her sore feet, which were a result of the radiation, and the fact that she was unable to walk. I listened carefully to Ann's words, after a time introducing her to the fact that I had brought two different sized Lyres. I offered Ann the smaller of the two, because of its more manageable size, and she spontaneously began to play scales. By affording her the opportunity to create music, I gave Ann the space to strengthen her self-confidence. She immediately began to enjoy the experience of playing. I showed her how to play single tones and we soon developed a musical dialogue on the two instruments; I would answer her with melodic 'motifs', surrounding her tones with fuller musical phrases. Ann remained relaxed in spite of her obvious concentration. At the end she exclaimed, *"That's really music!"* Ann told me that she intended to buy a Lyre and take lessons when she returned home. This provided a link with life outside the clinic. At the end of the session I showed Ann an exercise on the Lyre that would support her relaxed breathing. Our relationship became more intense through the non-verbal dialogue of this session.

During the fourth session Ann began to improvise alone; it felt as if something moved within her. Afterwards she talked, explaining that she didn't feel well. Ann allowed herself to feel anguished and lost. At the end I gave her the small Lyre with a song-book. It was my intention to allow Ann the opportunity to play and become more proficient in the time between our sessions. I had been greatly moved by Ann's improvising.

When I arrived for session five Ann was in bed. She was feeling unwell, suffering the effects of the radiation treatment. Ann's fingers had become so sore that she was unable to continue playing the Lyre. I had brought with me a glockenspiel tuned to the pentatonic scale. Placing the instrument on her bed, she began to improvise, my playing on the Lyre accompanying and mirroring her musical phrases. At the end I asked Ann if she enjoyed the music. Ann answered that the mode had left her feeling musically detached, that she knew instinctively what would be coming next. The trust built up through musical certainty in our musical relationship had been dictated by the tones of the pentatonic scale. I asked what the word trust meant to her. Ann's answer was that she trusted her husband, but not so much her children. She explained that *"My husband has given me trust in my life."* After this disclosure Ann went on to express her hope of becoming healthy and living again. The next 25 sessions were spent in a similar format, playing various instruments, singing and talking.

Four points are important in the discussion of these sessions:

- the strengthening of our relationship through the musical dialogue
- the discussion of difficult themes that Ann was unable to articulate before
- the chance for relaxation
- the opportunity to communicate through improvisation

After she returned home my contact with Ann became more irregular. Four weeks later, however, she was admitted to another ward. Ann immediately asked to see me. When I arrived she was suffering from psychosis caused by Morphium. Her mental state was poor.

The aim of our work up until this point had been to accompany her life as long as she still had hope. This first phase was crucial in providing the basis for an ongoing music therapy relationship. Ann stopped playing instruments now and only sang. I sang and played, giving her the opportunity to relax. Ann's intense verbal explorations continued. She asked to sing all the songs during the time we had spent together in music therapy. During our last session, Ann requested an aria by Mozart, asking me to sit on the bed and hold her hand. This was significant as up until now Ann had always kept a physical distance between us. At the end of the aria Ann seemed very relaxed. She ended the session by thanking me for everything that we had shared during our time together.

65

Three days later Ann died.

Elizabeth

Case study

Through the description of a single session, using specific vocal techniques, I would like to demonstrate the effectiveness of the use of the voice in music therapy.

Elizabeth and I had music therapy sessions for five years until she died. Over the years she developed tumours in her stomach which were inoperable. The session that I want to describe was difficult as Elizabeth had severe pains in her stomach. She suffered from intense nausea, particularly after eating. Arriving in her room I asked permission to place my hand on her stomach. Elizabeth accepted my physical closeness, allowing me to sit cross-legged opposite her while I put my hand on the most painful part. Touching her without applying pressure, I moved my hand clockwise around her stomach. Concentrating my inner and outer strengths on her reaction, I sang warm deep phrases, letting my breath carry the sound. The voice was born through breathing. Sounds and tones are elements of singing through breathing. Here I used both approaches.

After 20 minutes Elizabeth began to feel less sick. Her body relaxed and with my hand I could feel her more relaxed breathing. Elizabeth no longer complained about the pain. I continued to move my hand and sing. This was followed by a time for relaxation during which Elizabeth described her strengthening. She became more and more lively, eventually exclaiming *"How can this be true? I felt so ill all day, and now I feel better only because you are singing and your hand is lying on my stomach"*. She repeated this statement several times.

This example showed how it is possible to alleviate pain and nausea through singing and touch.

Comments

These three studies show the diversity of music therapy approaches available when working with the dying and their families. Florian's need for receptive music and the subsequent effect this therapeutic process had upon his mother highlight the need for an intense openness on the part of the music therapist. Rather than a three-way communication, two individual relationships developed. What does this reveal about the intense needs of patients with dying children and

66

how best can we adapt music therapy to meet the needs of both patient and families effectively in the face of death and dying? Ann highlights the potential for re-establishing musical abilities when faced with a terminal diagnosis and the power improvisation has to extend the music therapy relationship to deeper levels of expression. The use of pre-composed songs, the relevance of their lyrics and the potential they have for personal assessment are also represented. Questions in this example are raised in connection with differing clinical methods and how best they can be moulded to provide the most effective therapeutic approach. Finally, in the case of Elizabeth, we are reminded of the power of combining simple touch and voice. The clinical elements described in this paper are in themselves not new. What is highlighted, however, is the need for a balanced practice that will allow for a sensitivity of therapeutic process.

Reference

1. de Saint-Exupéry A (1982). *The Little Prince*. Pan Books Ltd, London.

Part Three

Philosophy and Spirituality

Music and Emotion in Palliative Care: Accessing Inner Resources

Deborah Salmon MA MTA CMT
Montreal, Canada

Introduction

During the past 10 years, working as a music therapist in the Palliative Care Service of Montreal's Royal Victoria Hospital, I have repeatedly observed and been impressed by how readily music evokes emotions. Patients laugh, cry, play, sing and speak deeply about their lives during music therapy sessions. There seems to be an interaction between music and emotion. I began to wonder: are there common elements in music and emotion? Might these be the factors which enable music to elicit and facilitate emotional expression? If so, how do we best use this phenomenon for therapeutic gain? And what are the underlying principles or values that guide our clinical work? In exploring these questions the schema on the following page was developed (fig 1).

It seems that music and emotion are woven of similar fabric, allowing one to resonate deeply with and give voice to the other. Both use symbolic means of expression: they are symbolic languages. Unlike verbal language, music and emotion may contain simultaneous, even conflicting themes, ideas or moods. They move through time, not space, and are constructed of relationships, with a continuous dynamic interplay between tension and resolution.[1] These five shared characteristics will be elaborated upon.

The music therapist brings skill, presence and music to the clinical situation through various interventions (song choice, singing, improvisation, etc), activating the resonance between music and emotion. A therapeutic process is thus facilitated through which people may experience greater breadth and depth of feeling, find a means of expression and work through some of their difficulties.

This is the essence of clinical work. Yet we must be further guided by a larger goal; that of helping people to access their own inner senses of well-being or meaning. Although highly individual, this process essentially involves

71

Figure 1: Music and emotion: assessing inner resources

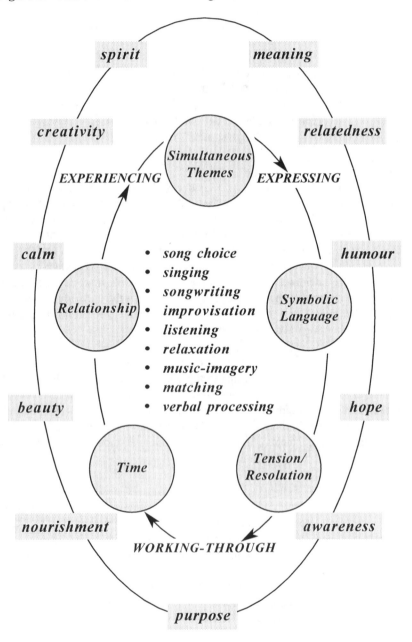

experiencing a sense of purpose, meaning, awareness, relatedness, spirit, beauty, calm, hope, nourishment, humour or creativity. Such experiences, when internalized, become part of a repertoire of personal resources. In the moments of connecting with these inner resources, it becomes possible to transcend the emotional and physical pains of terminal illness.

Words, being linear in nature, often fail to convey the multidimensional impact of music and of emotion. The theoretical ideas presented here are necessarily reductionist, looking at parts of the whole. In an effort to gain a fuller understanding, however, I shall alternate between these and the story of Jacques, interspersing examples of his struggle, growth, courage and creativity throughout the music therapy process.

Jacques
Jacques, barely able to move or speak, used several music therapy techniques (song choice, songwriting, listening, improvisation, and verbal processing) to share his inner life. In doing so he experienced a range of emotion and found ways to work through some of his anger and sadness. He drew upon his resources; humour, intelligence, and capacity to connect with and give to others, to find greater hope and meaning in his living and dying.

When Jacques arrived on our palliative care unit, he was 56 years old and suffering from end-stage amyotrophic lateral sclerosis (ALS), or motor neurone disease. Jacques was quadriplegic and dysarthric. He had some movement of his right hand, was fed through a gastric tube, and his slurred speech was difficult to understand. Jacques was initially very anxious. He was impatient and demanding with the staff and his wife, and reported a great fear of choking as well as fear and frustration at not being able to speak. On the third day of admission to our unit a nurse noted in the chart that music was important to Jacques. We were asked to see him in the hope that music therapy could help reduce his anxiety.

Simultaneous Themes
Music and emotion both have the capacity to carry several moods or feelings simultaneously. Various musical elements may be employed to convey different moods in a single musical composition. The Jewish song, Tumbalalaika, for example, contains happy lyrics in a waltz rhythm, sung to a poignant melody in a minor key. Similarly, people often experience mixed, even conflicting feelings.

Susan, our music therapy intern, and I went with guitar, flute and songbooks to assess Jacques. To my surprise, given the irritability with which he'd greeted most staff members, he welcomed us warmly. We learned that Jacques had never played an instrument but that he loved popular and classical music. He accepted our offer of live music and immediately requested the song 'My Way'. We played it with a definite rhythm, emphasizing the lyrics. Jacques smiled at my suggestion that perhaps 'I'll do it my way' was the message he was trying to communicate to our team. Because we were having difficulty understanding his speech, Jacques shakily wrote the title to his next request, 'Send In The Clowns'. As we played and sang, Jacques shut his eyes. He appeared to be listening intensely. I was struck not only by the combination of sadness, irony, bitterness and beauty in the song, but also particularly by the lyrics; 'Isn't it bliss, don't you approve, one who keeps tearing around, one who can't move. Where are the clowns, send in the clowns...'. Sharing my perceptions with Jacques, I asked him if his experience wasn't somehow similar to those lyrics. I reflected that it must be difficult to have people 'tearing around' him when he couldn't move. Jacques looked at us deeply and confirmed the personal relevance of the songs he'd chosen. He ended the session by telling us that he hoped there would be music at his time of death.

In the above session, Jacques used song choice, listening, and some verbalization as a means of conveying some of his internal experience. The first song seemed to express his anger and frustration as well as a wilfulness of spirit. The second song suggested that beneath his anger and bitterness lay great sadness. Finally, in this first session Jacques acknowledged that he would soon die and expressed the hope that he could do so with music present. Anger, wilfulness, sadness, hope; these different emotions could be revealed through and contained by the music. It seemed that Jacques had a need to express these feelings and that, as his verbal capacities decreased, music might offer him another avenue of communication. We also hoped that creative expression, as well as access to the nourishment that music seemed to provide him, might help decrease Jacques' anxiety.

Symbolic Language

Music has often been referred to as a symbolic language; it speaks to us without necessarily using words, appeals to the unconscious mind, and elicits images, sensations, memories and feelings. There is an ambiguous quality to music, akin to that of emotional experience. We may not find the exact words for our feelings, but express them symbolically through our images (e.g. dreams), actions, bodies, thoughts, and associations. Perhaps it is this shared ambiguity which allows music to contain such a wide range of feeling.

As verbal expression was becoming increasingly difficult for Jacques and because he continued to express anxiety and frustration, we offered him the opportunity to improvise on instruments. Jacques was interested; we positioned him in his bed with a conga drum in the centre, pentatonic tone bells to his right, and a tambourine to his left. Jacques was able to grasp a mallet and, with the limited movement in his right hand, reach all instruments. He began with the bells, tentatively picking out a melody which I began to mirror on the flute. He then moved to the tambourine and soon settled into a steady rhythm punctuated by occasional short bursts of loud beating on the conga. Susan and I followed, on guitar and flute, reflecting and supporting Jacques' playing. When we finished, Jacques spontaneously entitled the improvisation 'Nowhere to go but to Heaven'. He continued; 'Heaven in my mind...every day will be the same...there won't be any bad days...for eternity'.

Jacques used the instruments to express his feelings symbolically. He chose a steady rhythm to portray the unchanging nature of 'heaven in his mind', a striking contrast to the change and loss of control which he was experiencing. He didn't speak about other parts of the improvisation, but I wondered if his short bursts of conga playing were expressions of anger, perhaps because he did have 'nowhere to go but to heaven'. Again, this improvisation afforded Jacques a way to experience and symbolically to express a mix of feelings (anger, resignation, hope...). The music served to hold this expression, allowing Jacques access to his creativity, and hopefully helping him further to come to terms with his situation.

Song choice also continued to provide a means of indirect communication for Jacques and for Carole, his wife. Carole often requested 'You've Got A Friend', a song which clearly conveyed her ongoing love and support.

Tension/Resolution
Both music and emotion are born of a continuous dynamic interplay between tension and resolution. In music, tension and resolution are formed through dissonant and consonant harmonies, rising and falling melodies, changes in rhythm, tempo, and dynamics. In emotional life, from birth we experience need and satisfaction, fear and reassurance, conflict and resolution. People who are terminally ill may experience an increase of tension and anxiety as their disease progresses and death approaches. The wish or need for comfort and resolution is thus often felt more poignantly.

Jacques was actively using our music therapy services. He requested songs and classical music, listened to tapes from our cassette library, improvised when he had the physical energy, and talked about his living and dying. His anxiety appeared to decrease as he adjusted to living on our unit and his trust in our team grew. We began to improvise music to some of Jacques' thoughts which led to his use of songwriting. In a session which took place three weeks after his admission, Jacques painstakingly dictated the words to 'Just A Man'. Susan set it to a simple harmonic structure (figure 2).

Figure 2

Just A Man

Don't try to understand what you cannot understand,
Learn to live with pain, don't try to be a hero
Just be a man.
Don't be afraid to cry when you're in pain or scared,
Loved ones and friends, quite a few they are, shall understand
You are only a man.
When the time shall come for suffering and pain to end
Don't be mad or sad, smile and say goodbye;
And then and there you shall become more than just a man,
More than just a man.

To me, this song is indicative of 'working-through' in therapy. Jacques was clearly facing the difficulties of his situation, acknowledging his fear, sadness, anger and pain looking for a way to live with greater peace and acceptance. There is tension, seeking for resolution, but also something deeper. Jacques seemed to sense that by fully accepting his situation, including his death, he might somehow transcend his suffering and 'become more than just a man'. At the end of the session in which Jacques dictated the above words, he requested the Beatles' song 'Let It Be', which also speaks of the wisdom of acceptance. Jacques seemed to be accessing his own inner resources, his own depth and wisdom.

Time

Music is the organized movement of sound through time. Emotions are experienced moment to moment as they move through time. Perhaps it is this shared quality of movement through time which helps people stay in the 'here-and-now' of ongoing emotion within the music therapy experience. In palliative care, time is a key issue. There is the awareness that the remaining lifetime is

Figure 2: 'Just A Man'

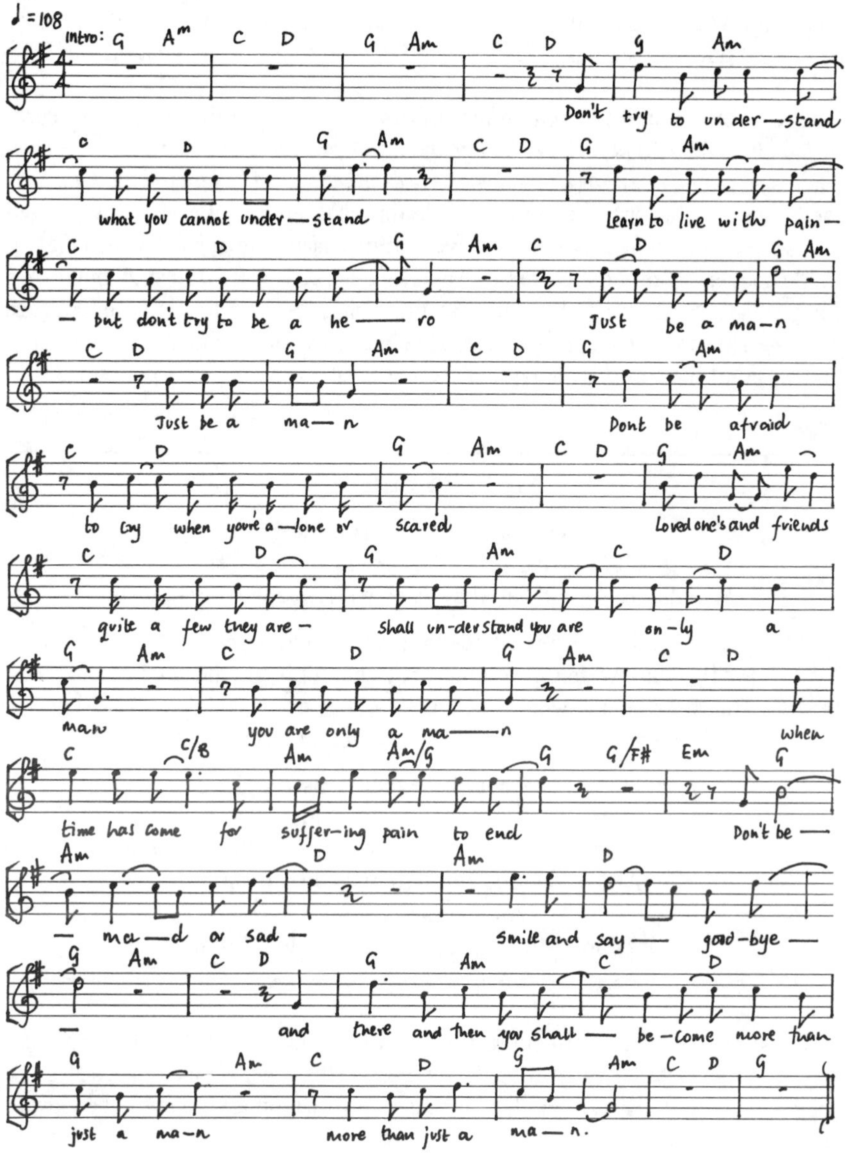

short, time may pass slowly in hospital, and the person's 'tempo' may be slowed due to weakness and medication. Finally, perception of the passage of time may be altered due to pain, anxiety, a changed mental status or medication.

Jacques worked hard to come to terms with his shortened lifespan. In an early session he said: *"When you lose a grandma or grandpa you lose the past, when you lose a friend or spouse, you lose the present. So me, I'm leaving the future..."* Jacques was also sensitive to musical rhythm and tempo. We've already noted his use of a steady rhythm in the 'Heaven' improvisation to depict an unchanging, stable heaven. A month before his death, Jacques composed a second, humorous song called 'Sick and Full of It'. In this song, dictated to his wife, Jacques described his bowel care. He requested that we use a blues progression, increasing the tempo of the song as the lyrics describe laxatives taking effect (figure 3):

Figure 3

Sick and Full of It

Here I am, sick and bedridden,
Not knowing if it's the beginning or the end
Wondering why in hell they're so worried about my bowel!

Right away they decide to use fibre and prune juice,
But I know damn well that they shall only get the smell.
But these people won't forgive, here they come with laxatives,
Followed by the big artillery, enemas and suppositories.

And then I could see their satisfied grin
As I was filling the bowl to the rim. Oh yeah.
Now that I know that an apple a day won't keep the doctor away,
At least a good shit will make him happy.
And let me also say
That people who don't give a shit end up full of it.

Jacques' frustration and discontent with his illness and the limits of his treatment are evident in these lyrics. Although still present, his anger is transformed through song and humour. He is not only able to express what otherwise might be viewed as open hostility, but we, the staff, are able to hear it and recognize Jacques' fighting spirit. These songs began to be used in different ways; they were played at our multidisciplinary team meeting and placed in the staff communication book. Jacques allowed me to present them in a course I was teaching, and he

Figure 3: 'Sick and Full of It'

repeatedly requested copies for friends and family. The songs remain a wonderful teaching tool.

Time played another factor in our interventions with Jacques. In his last days, as Jacques lay comatose, we often played music for him. We played the music he had requested and enjoyed, the songs he had composed, songs that his wife requested, and music improvisations. The improvised music used the rhythm of Jacques' breathing as a guiding tempo. Any sounds he made became tonal guides. This technique, which I call 'matching', demands a great deal of concentration and presence as the person's breathing, his or her ebbing life force, is the point of contact and the basis of music-making. I have, at times, felt deeply connected to the dying person in these moments. It is not uncommon for the person's rate of breathing to change, usually becoming slower and more regular. On occasion, death has occurred during the live music. Although one can never know for certain, it is my impression that music may sometimes facilitate this final phase of dying. It seems somehow to support the person in letting go of life and moving toward death. We were not present at Jacques' death, however in his last days his facial expression changed while we played 'Send in the Clowns', and Carole noted, *"he knows we're here"*.

Relationship

Music is the relationship of sounds through time. It is created by people, for people. Countless musical compositions and songs have been inspired by relationships and the feelings they engender. Emotional life, too, exists in the arena of relationships, to oneself and to others, in the past, present and future. Music has the ability to connect people emotionally. In palliative care music may help alleviate the sense of aloneness which patients and their loved ones sometimes experience. Music therapy, then, becomes a valuable tool for addressing the complexities of human relationships.

In Jacques' story, we see examples of music facilitating communication and expression in relationships. In the first session, Jacques chose the song 'Send in the Clowns', which portrays sadness and bitterness in relationship to another. Carole, his wife, responded continually with her message of support: 'You've Got a Friend'. Jacques' songs were a legacy that he was pleased to leave to family and friends - a personal gift that was precious to all. Confined to bed with extremely limited movement or speech, he nonetheless extended himself further, wanting 'others to learn from my songs', and suggesting that 'Sick and Full of It' be played for doctors whenever the opportunity arose. Our therapeutic relationship with Jacques was built through a sharing of the nourishing and expressive capacities of music. It allowed us to be there for and with him during the last months and days of his life, and to provide support to his wife. Most importantly, however, music supported and facilitated Jacques' relationship to his own inner resources. It helped him connect to and use his sense of purpose, grace, intelligence, spirit and wit.

Pilot Study

The experiences of Jacques and others with whom we have worked over the years suggest that music therapy contributes to the well-being of terminally ill patients. In an attempt to assess this impact objectively, a pilot study was designed, measuring on a self-report scale, patients' physical and emotional states before and after a music therapy session. In this study, a convenience sample of 15 terminally ill cancer patients reported statistically significant improvements in both physical and emotional realms after music therapy, with greater improvement occurring in the emotional realm.

Criteria for patients' participation in this study included admission to the Palliative Care Unit of the Royal Victoria Hospital, agreement to participate in music therapy and the study, ability to speak French or English, and sufficient strength and mental acuity to complete the questionnaire.

A simple questionnaire was created, to be filled out by each patient immediately before and after a music therapy session. It asked them to complete the statements 'Physically, I feel ....' and 'Emotionally, I feel ....' on a numerical scale ranging from 0 (extremely bad) to 10 (extremely good). It further asked for words describing how they felt in the two realms. A second form documented the therapist's observations, techniques used in each session, and verbal and nonverbal responses of the patient.

The music therapy interventions addressed patients' individual needs. No two were alike. The sessions, however, lasted a mean of 34 minutes and employed an average of three techniques.

The findings in 15 patients are presented in figure 4. Responses to the question 'Physically I feel ....' were as follows:

- 3 (20%) patients reported feeling physically worse after a music therapy session
- 3 (20%) reported feeling the same
- 9 (60%) reported feeling better

81

Figure 4: Music therapy survey data

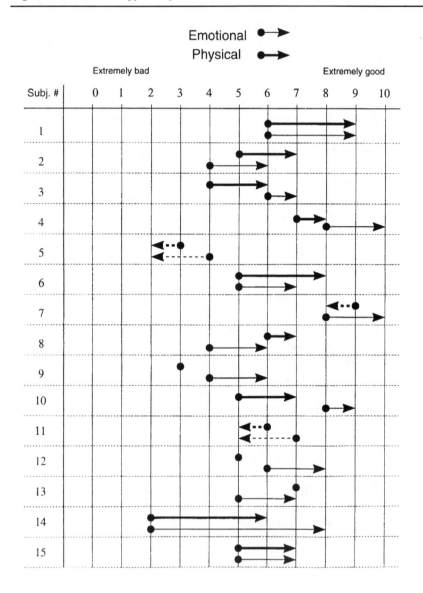

Where patients felt physically better, their scores increased by 1-4 points. Where they felt worse, their scores decreased by only one point. For the total sample, the physical scores increased by a mean of 1.1 points after a music therapy session, which was found to be statistically significant (T=2.75, p=0.02).

Responses to the question, 'Emotionally, I feel ....' were more dramatic:

- 2 patients (13%) reported feeling emotionally worse after a music therapy session

- 0 reported feeling the same

- 13 (87%) reported feeling better

Where patients felt emotionally better, their scores increased by 1-6 points. Where they felt worse, their scores decreased by two points. The patients' emotional scores increased by a mean of 1.67 points after a music therapy session, which was found to be highly statistically significant (T=3.44, p= 0.004).

This pilot study demonstrated the potential of a simple questionnaire to quantify subjective responses to music therapy in terminally ill patients. The size of the sample and method of sampling (convenience) preclude extrapolation of the findings to other settings. Furthermore, the results must be interpreted with caution since in the majority of cases (10 out of 15 patients) the questionnaire was given to the patient by the therapist rather than an independent observer. (Patients were told that their completely honest answers to these questions would be most helpful). While the significant impact on emotional well-being is of particular interest, these findings do not tap the full range of response to music therapy.

Conclusion
This study did not assess music therapy's ability to help terminally ill people access their inner resources and connect to a sense of greater meaning. Nonetheless, to have demonstrated a greater sense of well-being after music therapy is an important beginning. Perhaps these preliminary findings, along with the clinical stories of music therapy with this population, will shed a ray of light on the powerful and often magical interactions of music, emotion, spirit, living and dying.

Reference
1. Salmon, Deborah (1993). Music and emotion in palliative care. *Journal of Palliative Care*; *9(4)*: 48-52.

Acknowledgements

I would like to express my gratitude to the Royal Victoria Hospital's Palliative Care Service, and particularly to its director, Dr Balfour Mount, for his unstinting support of music therapy. Tremendous appreciation goes to Susan Phillips for composing the music to Jacques' songs and for her invaluable contributions to the clinical work. I would also like to thank Dr Robin Cohen for her research expertise which guided the pilot study, Robert Wadniki for generously sharing his computer skills and Sue Murphy for her help with data collection. Many friends and colleagues have offered encouragement along the way. Special thanks go to Connie Isenberg-Grzeda, Debbie Carroll and Aliki Thomas for their editorial comments, and to Garry Beitel for his love, support and hours of childcare. Last but not least, I wish to express my appreciation to Jacques and Carole for both sharing in the process and allowing me to present the resultant material.

The Role of Music Therapy in Meeting the Spiritual Needs of the Dying Person

Kirstin Robertson-Gillam BA RMT RN
Eastwood, Australia

Introduction

This paper examines how music, relaxation, song lyrics and creative artwork can induce a shift in consciousness in the dying person allowing them to release physical pain and emotional suffering. By meeting these physical and emotional needs, it is possible to alleviate much of the distress that occurs as a result of the terminal illness.

Music with dialogue can help the mind and body to relax. In this altered state, images and suppressed emotions may surface. The music used for assisting this process is carefully selected for its rhythm, melody and timbre. Similarly, the dialogue focuses on the special needs of the dying person. These release processes which can be brought about through the application of music are viewed within the context of Maslow's[1] needs hierarchy. They are also compared with Peck's[2] spiritual development theory and Kubler-Ross'[3] stages of responses to the dying process. These correlated theories, highlighted by case histories, help to raise the understanding of the important role that music therapy can play with dying people.

Music and Palliative Care

In the field of palliative care, non-traditional approaches, among them music therapy, are now being recognised as valid ways of easing pain and suffering. There is a growing awareness that music has a significant impact on the body, mind and human emotion. Palliative care is beginning to recognize the psycho-dynamic nature of music and its usefulness when treating physical and psychological symptoms.

Music can reflect, reveal and facilitate deep emotional states, often at an unconscious level. When inner feelings surface through music it can affect the

85

right brain (through non-logical processes), the response being spontaneous. It is within these spontaneous moments that the spiritual essence is revealed. The choice may be to push the issues back into the sub-conscious mind or to explore them further. Music therapy can act as a vehicle for psychological resolution or as a diversion from distressing physical symptoms. Either way, music can meet needs at many levels.

Spirituality

Spirituality is a concept that has been ill-defined in Western culture. The Collins English Dictionary describes it as 'relating to the spirit or soul and not to physical nature or matter'. Hay[4] referred to spirituality as 'a capacity for transcending one's working realities (ie, physical, sensory, rational and philosophical) in order to love and be loved within one's communities; to give meaning to existence; and to cope with the exigencies of life'. According to this definition, *spiritual distress* is a condition in which a person can no longer find any meaning in life and is unable to cope with or transcend the reality of the ramifications within the terminal disease.

Amenta and Bohnet[5] outlined positive and negative concepts of spirituality which, when understood, can help ease suffering and spiritual distress (as defined above). Emotional states of guilt and fear can be deeply embedded within the spiritual essence of an individual. Accordingly, they threaten to raise survival issues[1] involving the physical symptoms of the disease as well as safety, love and belonging needs[1] involving one's social surrounding. This in turn, can cause the person to magnify their physical pain. Music therapy can help validate these negative emotions, and thus lead toward some kind of spiritual resolution. This can be achieved by using relaxation techniques with appropriate dialogue and music, or playing live or recorded music. Improvisation can also allow expression leading to some degree of cathartic release.

The positive aspects of spirituality[5] ease pain, suffering and distress if the patient is given the 'tools' to deal with them. Such positive concepts as love, hope, peace and relatedness are states of mind which can lessen the intensity of negative feelings. Music can be offered to aid the change from negative to positive. It can bring families and friends together, bridging the gaps caused by the fear, guilt, pain etc. Thus hope and peace can become more viable states of mind. In song lyrics and melodies (both popular and classical) the clients can validate their lives by finding elements in them that remind them of themselves; bringing back a sense of identity, family and culture.

Suffering, Pain and Stress

Suffering can be emotional and physical. Pain and suffering are frequently viewed as being connected. However, a person may suffer extensively from psychological trauma without experiencing physical pain. According to Chapman and Garvin[6], suffering is a complex condition that involves emotional and psychological states as well as unpleasant responses which involve 'a perceived threat to the self within an enduring psychological state'.[6] As a result, an individual may contract a life threatening illness without extensive suffering, or may suffer from extreme psychological trauma without physical conditions.

Suffering, from the author's perspective, involves the deep seated negative emotions such as paralysing fear, guilt and anger which are experienced as a response to a life threatening illness. These emotions originate within the spiritual essence of a person and constitute spiritual distress.

Physical pain is the body's response to trauma and acts as a warning device. The nervous stimulus that causes the sensation of pain is generally related to tissue damage and is often accompanied by an emotional experience. According to Fonberg[6], emotion is a process of the nervous system that determines which stimuli are desirable for the survival of the organism. Consequently, it can be seen that the experience of pain for the terminally ill person is not only distressing in its own right, but is also capable of reinforcing negative emotions (mentioned previously) that raise awareness of the end of life.

The perception of pain determines how severe and intense it will be. This perception is derived from the inner processes or spiritual centre. Pain can lead to anxiety which produces muscle tension and more intense pain. Furthermore, anxiety can cause changes in normal breathing patterns, thereby reducing the amount of oxygen in the muscle tissues. The result is increased pain and anxiety. Music is able to break this cycle by decreasing anxiety and inducing relaxation. As the patients become relaxed, they may experience images and sensations leading to a sense of emotional and spiritual resolution.

Stress is a necessary element for stable living. However, stress overload typically produces negative emotion. Chronic pain in terminal illness causes stress that can invade the human spirit and allow loss of control over one's environment. A situation of 'learned helplessness'[7] can be the result. This increases suffering as the patient loses hope and feels trapped in an impossible situation. Accordingly, suffering is increased at a deep spiritual level. Music can reflect these negative emotions allowing the patient to reach different levels of perception. At the deepest level, the qualities of music can ease spiritual distress.

The Stage Theories

Theories of spiritual and psychological growth indicate that change is essential. It is how the individual copes with change that determines the levels of needs and degrees of spiritual distress. When the theories of Maslow[1], Peck[2] and Kubler-Ross[3] are correlated with the process of music therapy[8], a therapeutic approach can be devised to meet the spiritual needs of the dying person.

Maslow's hierarchy of needs[1] postulates that an individual's basic needs must be met first before progression to higher levels can be achieved. Peck's theory of spiritual development[2] argues that people pass through three stages of spiritual growth before they reach the fourth and final stage of mysticism or spiritual transcendence. He calls the first stage *chaotic*, indicating a spiritually underdeveloped, unprincipled and self-serving individual. The second or *formal* stage views God as an 'external, transcendent being' who is all-controlling. The rules and rituals of formalised religion are vitally important. The third, *sceptic* stage is one of questioning formalised belief system and other spiritual dilemmas. The final fourth stage Peck[2] labels as *mystic* and is where a person is prepared to explore the deeper meanings of life and experience their own inner spiritual depths.

Kubler-Ross' theory[3] postulates that people experience five emotional response levels when faced with grief, loss and dying. *Denial* is the first response which can be a coping mechanism that protects the person from the full implications of the terminal illness. Many people can remain at this stage as reality is too difficult to contemplate. The *anger* stage tends to be a time when a patient projects their anger onto others such as doctors. Because of its powerful nature, anger can provide energy for working through issues and getting things done. The *bargaining* stage often involves making bargains with God as the person still holds on to hope. The *depression* stage is characterised by a full realisation of the implications of the terminal illness. *Acceptance* can occur as the last stage when the individual begins to come to terms with the inevitability of impending death.

Music and the Stage Theories

Music can facilitate the mind and body at Maslow's physiological level by the use of repetitive rhythms. This effects changes in the heart beat, respiration and galvanic skin response. For instance, the basso continuo of Pachelbel's *Canon in*

D helps to ground the body and still the mind by its even, predictable chordal progressions and repetitive rhythmic structures.

The melody and harmony of music can also entrain the mind at Maslow's safety level. This opens up the inner processes of imagery and past memories. For example, Haydn's *Adagio* movement from the *Cello Concerto in C, No.1*, can facilitate feelings of safety and warmth. These have been found by some patients to be spiritually nurturing. Furthermore, this type of music can induce relaxation and evoke imagery.

The timbre of the musical instruments is important. For example, brass band music is reflective of energetic states, such as anger (as perceived by the listener). This is because the music contains lively repetitive rhythms and strong textures. In contrast, the flute is known to lift the human spirit, whilst the violin can soothe the emotions.

The correlation of Maslow[1], Peck[2] and Kubler-Ross'[3] theories appears to validate the release processes of music therapy when applied to dying people. They can help to identify why some patients respond to their environment in chaotic, negative ways. The theories highlight the important role of music therapy in palliative care and serve to pinpoint the most appropriate intervention that will meet the dying person's spiritual needs.

Case Histories

Mrs T

Mrs T was a 59 year old woman, suffering from metastatic melanoma. She arrived at the hospice in a state of anxiety and excitability. The primary need was to control her pain and review her family and social situation. She was referred to music therapy because she had been a radio announcer on a classical music community radio station. It was felt that music might be able to relieve her anxiety.

On meeting Mrs T, I found that she was in constant cycles of conversation and activity. She was not still for a moment. We discussed her preferences in music and I supplied her with a tape player and tapes. During my first few visits [the contact stage[8]], Mrs T. made her needs known to me by body and verbal language. We decided that recorded music was not the medium for Mrs T as her restless, anxious spirit could not relax on its own.

Her immediate problem was to manage her pain which was not responding well to conventional medication (Maslow's first stage[1]). She indicated that she was in denial about the serious nature of her illness by constantly focusing on making phone calls and plans about how she would manage 'when she went home' (Kubler-Ross' first stage[3]). She was too sick to return home and this was evident from the time of her admission to the hospice.

listening to life + musical excerpts

Live keyboard music (Bach, Pachelbel and Mozart) at the bedside offered 'time out' from constant talking, both on the telephone and with staff and visitors. Music also became a distracter from the pain. The music seemed most effective at medication times. Music, reassurance and relaxation were effective for inducing a sense of calm. Other needs, such as eating, were successfully met with music. For instance Bach's *Air on the G String* in D major gave Mrs T permission to eat without talking to her endless stream of visitors.

urgency

The awareness stage (Bailey's second stage[8]) was characterised with a session incorporating imagery and music. Mrs T was able to relax with keyboard music and verbal suggestions. During this time, Mrs T 'saw', in a visualisation, her husband who had died three years previously. She had not dealt with her grief adequately, and after this music therapy session she was able to speak about her feelings associated with his death. She expressed anger towards God (Kubler-Ross' second stage[3]) and began to speak about her religious belief in a formal punitive God (Peck's second stage[2]). Mrs T was able to continue exploring other emotional issues in subsequent music therapy sessions.

Counselling sessions with Mrs T's daughter revealed relief at the release of the grief associated with her father's death. This brought mother and daughter closer together (Maslow's love and belonging needs). She began to restrict the chaplain's visits so that she could explore her scepticism about her formal religious background (Peck's stage three[2]). The chaplain represented God to her and she did not want that contact during this period of scepticism. Afterwards, bargaining with God occurred as Mrs T became less anxious and tense (Kubler-Ross' third stage[3]).

These sessions were followed by depression (Kubler-Ross' fourth stage[3]). This caused Mrs T to withdraw socially by reducing her daily visitors.

90

Her struggle to convince her elderly mother of the terminal nature of her disease helped her to realize how seriously ill she was. Family and religious values all seemed to collapse at once as Mrs T wrestled with meeting her own needs. Music was chosen that might highlight her heightened emotions. These helped her to begin resolving emotional and psychological issues.

Once Mrs T convinced her mother that she was going to die, her levels of anxiety and fear gradually diminished. She began to see meaning in life from a moment-to-moment perspective. Her self-esteem became higher with an improvement in self respect (Maslow's self actualisation stage[1]; Kubler-Ross'[3] acceptance level and Bailey's resolution stage[8]). Even though Mrs T was able to resolve many emotional and social issues, it is difficult to know whether she progressed to Peck's mystic stage[2] or not. After resolving matters with her mother and seeing her newly born first grandchild, Mrs T lapsed into a coma and died a few days later. The dying period was supported by live music to relax her restless body movements.

Music played a central role in the last few months of Mrs T's life, bringing many threads of the tapestry together and helping her daughter to cope with her loss. (See figure 1 for a visual table of correlations of the three theories and Bailey's music therapy stages).

Mr E

Mr E was 55 years old when he found out he was dying from fast growing bowel cancer. He had never been sick in his life. The experience of being dependent was anathema to him. His doctor referred him to music therapy in order to reduce anxiety and help gain some insight and understanding of his disease. He was at the lowest level of all the stage theories.

My first visit with him was spent mainly adjusting and re-adjusting his pillows and bedclothes. I was finally able to give him a short music-based relaxation session using Pachelbel's *Canon in D*. He was amazed that he could experience imagery and attain the relaxation response so quickly. This built a trusting relationship. He was not so much in denial of his condition as he was in shock at the enormity of the ramifications of the disease. Over the next few weeks, Mr E related many stories about his life. He continued to receive music and relaxation

Figure 1: Comparison of three psychological theories with the
music therapy process

MASLOW	PECK	KUBLER-ROSS	BAILEY (Music therapy intervention)
Physiological	Chaotic	Denial	Contact
Safety	Formal	Anger	Awareness
To love & belong	Sceptic	Bargaining	Reassurance
Self-esteem		Depression	
Self Actualisation	Mystic	Acceptance	Resolution
Desire to know & understand			Questioning & discussion Inner self-expression
Aesthetic needs			

regularly. I tape recorded the session with dialogue so that he could use the tape at night when he became distressed This proved very effective, as reported by the night staff.

Mr E seemed to skip Kubler-Ross' anger stage and oscillated between Maslow's physiological and safety levels. His needs were met with the relaxation and medication. At the spiritual level, Mr E seemed to skip the formal and sceptic stages of Peck's theory and progressed to the mystic stage with imagery and visualisations. He began to establish a closer relationship with his brother who was his only family (Maslow's third stage).

Depression (Kubler-Ross' third stage) came when Mr E had two disturbing dreams in which he was falling to pieces and had to figure out how to put himself back together again. His awareness heightened as we began to interpret the meaning of his dreams (Bailey's second stage). During this awareness and depression stage, Mr E continually complained of being bored and empty. I decided to write down his words and suggested that he could put them to music in the form of a song. Mr E agreed.

The song lyrics expressed deep inner spiritual distress and suffering. They revealed a sense of helplessness over his condition and loss of meaning in his life.

> *Bored, empty, void.*
> *Bored, empty, too tired.*
> *Unhappy. No purpose.*
> *No sense of reasoning (repeat)*
> *Distressed, stressed out*
> *Distressed. Bored.*

> *My life was once in control.*
> *A perfect jigsaw picture.*
> *Then sickness befell me.*
> *My life in pieces (repeat)*
> *Empty, bored. Void, bored.*

[See figure 2 for the music]

93

Figure 2: 'Bored, Empty, Void'

After I had sung Mr E this song, he was shocked at what he had been expressing.

I felt he was able to reach a level of acceptance as he worked on resolving inner emotional issues. Occasionally he was able to relax to music at the bedside, but he responded best to the one-on-one contact that occurred during relaxation and imagery sessions.

His moment of self actualisation occurred when he realised that he could die with dignity and without fear. The culmination of these sessions was an imagery session with music in which I encouraged him to associate freely. The music chosen was the *Adagio* movement of Beethoven's *Piano Concerto No. 5 in E flat major, Opus 73* 'The Emperor'. I interpreted his imagery as indicating mental and spiritual detachment. The session helped Mr E come to terms with his impending death. His death was achieved with dignity, acceptance and peace.

Mr K

Mr K was a 29 year old man from the Australian bush. He was dying from a malignant localised form of cancer. Mr K had lived life in the fast lane with drugs, alcohol and 'good times'. He was (recently) married with a seven month old baby girl. No medication could control the depth of his pain. Music therapy was therefore recommended to help alleviate his pain. His doctor believed that it would close the gate to pain through distraction and sensory stimulation.[9]

Mr K responded to relaxation at once. A trusting relationship was immediately established.[8] Mr K was in denial of the terminal nature of his illness and was spiritually distressed, i.e. felt that he was distressed to the very depths of his being.

During the awareness stage, Mr K's needs were met by two collages to music where he explored aspects of his childhood. Most significant in the first collage was the appearance of a panda bear in the bottom right hand corner. He verbally expressed a hidden desire for a cuddly toy. With the help of the clinical nurse consultant, I was able to obtain a panda bear for him. The palliative care team became more aware of his needs to be loved. He was able to relate more openly with his wife and express his need to be physically touched. The social worker began to give her counselling about her own issues while Mr K continued to work with his issues in music therapy. Their relationship began to improve.

We explored song material together and compiled a personal song book of his favourite songs. The first song was *Blowin' in the Wind* by Bob Dylan. It helped him to think about his life and the meaning of it. For the first time, Mr K began to explore issues about the existence of God. The songs, *Bridge over troubled water* by Simon and Garfunkel and *Do you know where you're going to?* from *Mahogany* by Michael Masser expressed for him his anger and pain. They also brought to the surface issues of helplessness over his disease and his fear of death.

Mr K's denial of his condition was expressed and dealt with in his second collage where he dedicated a whole section, in the left hand side of the paper, to 'blowing up his cigarettes' because he said that he was going to give up smoking. However, he also put in a picture of a frog (which he said symbolised himself), a beautiful woman and baby. The imagery was reminiscent of the archetypal Beauty and the Beast story and expressed his feelings of ugliness inflicted as a result of the disease. He was able to work through these issues verbally with a growing acceptance of them.

During the three months in the hospice, Mr K moved between denial, depression and acceptance. He made many gains in personal insight and growth in the process of his therapy. He showed a desire to know and understand the mysteries of his illness and his life (Maslow's highest stage). His aesthetic needs became important and were met with collage and songs. He progressed from Peck's chaotic to formal stages when he began to explore the existence of God. This was Mr K's moment of self actualisation when he acknowledged to himself the existence of a higher power. In this moment, he found peace of mind and hope in a future after life. Mr K died to the sound of Pachelbel's *Canon* playing continuously, at his request.

Conclusion

These three case studies illustrate how spiritual distress can be alleviated with the help of music, song lyrics and collage. Spirituality represents the deepest level of human needs. Music in all its forms has been found to meet these needs. The stage theories are useful because they validate this phenomenon and are able to pinpoint what is going on for the patient and how we, as therapists, can

96

intervene. Accordingly, the relationships between pain, suffering, stress and loss of control can be clearly identified with the correlation of the stage theories.

Music therapy when applied to meet these emotional and physical needs is clearly effective at each stage. This approach appears to give a clearer picture of the overall physical and psychological state of the dying person.

The entrainment and release processes produced by music can assist and facilitate the dying process by alleviating spiritual distress. The spiritual aspect of music can be one of the most important therapeutic tools the music therapist has to offer a dying person. Music therapy can help the patients work through their psychological issues and find peace and acceptance.

Based on my own clinical experience, I have come to realise that music can only open the gateway for releasing the spirit. It is well known that people can override the effects of medications through sheer will power. Music, however, appears to be able to override the will because it works at many different levels simultaneously. For those who cling to fear and ego, music is often refused. Presumably, this is due to the innate knowledge that music has a powerful and intrusive influence on the human psyche.

Music is one of the most potent vehicles by which the human spirit can be released. It enhances quality of life and facilitates a peaceful death. In the death-denying philosophy of Western culture, music and creative arts are the most valuable ways of dealing with the dying process. They are the bridge between quality of life and quality of death.

References

1. Maslow AH (1954). *Motivation and personality*. Harper and Brother, USA.

2. Peck MS (1978). *The Different Drum*. Simon and Schuster, NY USA. pp187-200.

3. Kubler-Ross E (1968). *On Death and Dying*. Macmillan Publisher, NY USA.

4. Hay MW (1989). Principles in building spiritual assessment tools. *The American Journal of Hospice Care;* Sept/Oct.

5. Amenta M & Bohnet (1986). Spiritual Concerns. *Nursing care of the terminally ill*. Little Brown and Co, Canada. pp115-171.

6. Chapman CR & Gavrin J (1993). Suffering and its relationship to pain. *Journal of Palliative Care; 9(2)*: 5-13.

7. Seligman MEP & Maier SF (1967). Failure to escape traumatic shock. *Journal of experimental psychology;* 1974: 1-9.

8. Bailey LM (1984). The use of songs in music therapy with cancer patients and their families. *Music Therapy; 4 (1)*: 5-17.

9. McCaffery & Beeke (1989). *Pain: Clinical manual for nursing practice.* The CV Mosby Co, USA.

Select Bibliography

1. Cassell E (1982). The nature of suffering; the goals of medicine. *New England Journal of Medicine; 306*: 639-645.

2. Clark B (1991). Spirituality in the hospice setting. *Palliative Medicine; 5*: 151-154.

3. Frankl VE (1980). The meaning of suffering for the terminally ill. *Proceedings of the 3rd International seminar on Terminal Care.* Post-Graduate Board, Royal Victoria Hospital, McGill University, Montreal, Canada.

4. Frankl VE (1984). *Man's search for meaning.* Washington Square Press, USA.

5. Peck MS (1978). *The road less travelled.* Simon and Schuster, NY, USA.

6. Schroder-Shaker T (1992). The use of music in death and dying. *Music and Miracles.* Compiled by Campbell D. Quest Books, USA.

 7. Stepnick A & Perry T (1992). Preventing spiritual distress in the dying client. *Journal of Psychosocial Nursing; 30(1)*: 17-24.

8. Wylie ME & Bolm RC (1986). Guided Imagery and Music with Hospice Patients. *Music Therapy Perspectives; 3*: 25-28.

The Voice of the Sounding Bowl

Tobias Kaye
Buckfastleigh, UK

Editor's Comments

I was first introduced to the sounding bowl when I began work at Sir Michael Sobell House. The music therapist who was acting as adviser to the setting up of the post, Rachel Verney, had met Tobias at a craft fayre. She immediately recognised the therapeutic possibilities of using such instruments in music therapy. The hospice subsequently ordered a seven-string bowl just before my appointment. Since then, I have further acquired a 14-string bowl.

The sounding bowl does not resemble any formalised instrument. One of its main advantages is that people do not feel any sense of having to play it in an orthodox or proper manner. If I am meeting someone for the first time on the ward I will simply lay the bowl on the bed, often not mentioning its existence. Within a short time the client will normally reach out and begin either stroking the strings as they talk, or will focus on the bowl as the main theme for our opening verbal and/or musical dialogue. The sounding bowl can consequently become a subsidiary means to access the relationship or may become a central part of the therapeutic direction itself. I use the sounding bowl at many levels, from relaxation sessions through to delicately balanced work with people who are nearing death. I regard the sounding bowl as essential to my work in palliative care. Its sensitivities as an instrument, the beauty of its shape and texture of its surface all add to its personal qualities that are recognised and used to great effect by all people who play it.

The following paper describes the philosophical foundation to Tobias' work. It gives insight into the creative process of a wood craftsman struggling to find musical form. We are provided with a sense of the person behind such beautifully crafted and powerful instruments.

Not being a music therapist but a wood craftsman, I hope you will excuse me if my way of looking at music therapy differs from the usual. This paper describes my sounding bowls and why I make them. As a preface, I will start with something about my understanding of life.

Beginning with the premise that consciousness exists before birth and after death, one may infer that it is not dependent on physical manifestation. Some branches of biology view consciousness as a product of the body. I, however, view the body as a product of consciousness. Having created a body, consciousness embarks on a voyage of adventure and learning through isolation. Like any adventure this has inherent problems. At any point in the journey we may find ourselves unable or unsure how to proceed. Reminders of the origins and the goal of our journey can provide us with clues to our next step. Where can we find such reminders, and how can we establish contact, however tenuous with our origins and goals?

Music is one of the languages of healing. It has the power to provide this contact, if the musician is aware of the needs she or he is serving. As an instrument maker, I make it my task to be aware of the needs my instruments will be serving. I do this in the first instance through the image of consciousness and isolation on our journey. Secondly, I consider a sense of the temporarily lost, as I have been, and to some extent always am. I wish my instruments to serve as a link between our goals and origins and the situation in which we find ourselves. E.g. my instruments were born as an inspiration during one of the darker periods of my life. The making of each is still a juggling of these extremes of inspiration and despair. The forms of the bowls are for me an allegory of the human soul. For example the string tension stresses the wood. The stress increases the wood's resonant qualities. We do not reach our potential if we have not lived with stress.

The acoustic of the internal curve of the bowl arises from years of struggling to achieve forms that are visually harmonious. From the visual the audible comes forth. As a final step, I try to embody in each instrument my image of the person who will be using it, and the people they will be working with. Evidence that this consciousness also finds its embodiment comes from the number of users who have responded with enthusiasm to a particular bowl. Thus, step by step I prepare my bowls to work as bridges. For the client, this may be experienced as a bridge between a traumatised now and a clearer original consciousness or future resolution. For the therapist this may be experienced as the bowl assisting in developing a relationship with the client.

Two varieties of bowls have been developed. The wider type with its parallel stringing is enticingly easy to play and listen to. Its sound reaches out and embraces the player. This bowl can access deep levels, as all its users will testify. The deeper bowl with its fan shaped stringing is more intimate. It leads into inner depths reflected and opened to the soul's eye. These statements come from personal experience, from observing others and from conversations with therapists. The deep bowls can lead to realisation that allows acceptance and growth. If a person is closed to these realms this bowl may pass them by where wider types may be more accessible.

While there are historical antecedents for these instruments, discovered some years after making began, experts have identified them as unique in the recorded history of musical instruments, not least because the strings resound from the acoustic form as opposed to from above its top surface. This aspect is also allegorical. The shallower bowl harks back to Apollo's tortoiseshell instrument in which the Earth speaks to the sky, the deeper bowl to the Greek Lyre through which the Gods speak to the Earth and also to the scallop shell, symbol of the Pilgrim (journeying to find the birth of Venus, [i.e. the journey of self-knowledge to the fount of creative consciousness]).

Music therapy is, for me, an attempt to apply these arts of threshold-consciousness. The soul that struggles, feeling out of its depth, may be thrown a rope, a line, that connects it again to its divine origins. To the wearing of this rope I dedicate my efforts.

Form - Its Movement in Time and Space, Metamorphosis

You will hopefully be familiar with form in time, through music. The movement of a melody is form expressing itself in time. My work as a wood turner is to produce forms in space. When I first began turning wood I was delighted to find that the forms I made expressed a similar feeling as that which I had tried to express through poetry (a discontinued hobby). For me the wrestling of words into forms was the same effort as wrestling form into wood. The same forms, different mediums. On meeting a man with whom I had studied poetry, I took him to my workshop and showed him some bowls, and said, *"Look Paul, poetry in form"*. He said, *"Yes, very interesting - what are you doing for supper tonight?"* As yet, others could not see the link.

Within a year of starting wood turning, I noticed that I had stopped playing the piano. I regretted this, as I had enjoyed playing. I couldn't seem to find the time or interest to practise. Some years later when we moved down to Devon, for a month or two I didn't have a workshop - we were building it. I rushed out and bought a piano at an auction and started playing again. I was delighted to find that music was coming back into my life. However, once the workshop was completed I stopped playing the piano. It was only later that I realised that music, like poetry, had been transformed into the curves of bowl walls. Indeed, I then reconnected with the fact that in my early years I had sometimes lain in bed at night, transposing a phrase of a song into the swoop and life of a bowl's wall curve.

About the time of moving to Devon, someone quoted to me the philosopher-craftsman Professor David Pye, 'A form either sings where it stands or is silent forever'. I was immediately enthused. Yes, I thought, that's what I'm working for - a form that is so harmonious in its shape that it sings where it stands. That's what I work for - a form that has innate harmony, a harmony that is not loudly expressed but is richly implicit.

For years I worked on these themes. I choose woods that were particularly bland, so that my work hung or fell on its form. I let my customers judge with the cash whether I had achieved a beautiful shape or not (a bowl made from exotic wood will sell, however poorly shaped). I must admit that I finished this period with something of a sense of failure - none of the shapes I made were actually audible: one could put them on the table and they would sit still, they would not hum. However, one piece, not vastly dissimilar from the rest, was sitting on the piano. Having been made from wet wood it was in the process of drying and it suddenly split. The noise it made was so harmonious that two rooms rang for an instant. This can be partly explained by the piano it was resting on, but not fully. I came through from the kitchen to see what had made the wonderful sound.

Shortly after this, a composer friend picked up the bowl and was tapping the side of it and listening to the sound, he said *"This is a beautiful sound - can I borrow this to make some recordings?"* Later he echoed my own thoughts, *"You've got a natural acoustic in this space, you ought to do something to bring it out."* *"Yes"* I said, *"but what?"* *"Well, perhaps put a drum skin across it"*. I had thought of that, but the idea of hiding the whole of the inside and at least one third of the outside I'd struggled to make harmonious, with an opaque skin, did not appeal. Besides, I'd seen drums made by other people that sounded good and didn't have carefully-shaped interiors. Thus, I rejected this idea. I gave it some more thought over the next week, but couldn't come up with any means by which this interior acoustic could be made to speak.

102

Some time later I was sitting on my bed when the idea of stretching strings across a turned bowl suddenly came into my head. This was it, this was an idea which was visually exciting and had resonant potential. I made one bowl with strings and sold it quickly. My intention was to make something which was part way between a sculpture and an instrument.   More than a sculpture yet not an instrument. I did not want 'non musical' people to dismiss this object from their world by classifying it as an instrument. Thus, when my composer friend came again and said *"You could develop this. You could make these into more of an instrument"*, my reaction was not enthusiastic. I did collaborate with him, fitting eight guitar strings rather than four gut ones. Later this experience was useful, but on my third sounding bowl I returned to three gut strings. Trying to create something which was audibly, as well as visually, harmonious - in other words a sounding sculpture.

The next dozen instruments explored the question of resonant acoustics. I made deep ones, wide ones, bowls with thick walls and thin walls, bowls with rims that overhung or dipped back down into the bowl - always looking for a formula by which I could produce harmonious sounding bowls. The only conclusive result was that if I concentrated on the sound, it would indeed sound good.   If I approached it in an experimental frame of mind, or attempted to copy something that had previously been successful, the sound was weak. This made me think, *"How is it that the way I think and feel about the work has more influence on the sound than the obvious physical characteristics of the form?"* It seems to me that this is another case of form in action. Let me explain. Our thinking flows on in our mind whether we listen to it or not. It is only when we take our thinking and shape it to our service that it performs a useful function in the world. In other words, it is only when we give *form* to our thinking that it has an effect. This is similar to when you give form to a piece of music, or a piece of wood. It is the forms one experiences inwardly that determine how the forms one puts out (in wood or in music) can be used. The sound of music effects a person inwardly. The feeling the musician puts into playing effects the sound. The subtlest details of a bowl's curve effect the tone of the acoustic. The feelings of the turner effects the subtlest details of a bowls curve. Further, one can see how the tone of the bowls effects a person inwardly. I believe there is a link between how the hearer feels as he listens or plays and how the turner feels as he creates the curve.

There is a traceable line from player to listener or instrument maker to those who hear the instrument, but there is a similar, subtler link. A link that goes through transformation between expressing itself in early life and in another way later

103

on. Music becomes form becomes music. At all points, the starting is within the thinking and feeling. That which lives within me has transformed its mode of expression. Practising and turning are both necessary if the performance is to be good. If I do not prepare myself before making a sounding bowl, the results will not be what I seek. The relationship I have with the person who commissions a sounding bowl influences the subtleties of tone. The relationship of commissioner to the finished piece is usually immediate and strong. When making a bowl as a commission, I will take into consideration the person who is to use the bowl, the type of work it is for, and how they approach their work. Out of this comes a bowl which suits them and their needs. This seems to be a subtle instance of forms moving from person to person, to object and back.

There are some other aspects of this question which are more abstruse. When a bowl is first strung, the tone tends to be that of metal strings on wood, whereas over the first few weeks the shape alters to take the stress of the strings. During this process the tone will mellow and become one, so that the instrument sings with one voice. Note also, that timber grown under stress produces a better tonal quality than timber grown without stress. (Many trees experience stress in their growth, either by having to grow against wind, or a steep slope. All trees have stress in one part of their grain, for instance, close to the junction of a large branch). Thus, I use wood that has been stressed when making a bowl. I liken this again, to the human soul. A person who has learned to experience stress usually seems to have a greater depth and vibrancy than a person who has not. Thus, in different ways, you have the coming forth of beauty out of stress. Stressed grain is visually more beautiful than straight grain. Stressed grain yields a richer tone than straight grain. The bowl's form, stressed and bent by the strings' pull enriches the tone. The stressed human soul deepens and enriches its nature. Is there a link between the balance of stress in the musical bowls and their therapeutic use?

I am not the first person to consider form. Sheldrake's[1] scientific works on the birth of form (morphogenesis), give examples of the birth of form in thinking, feeling and biology. He has been influential on my thinking. Sheldrake[1] discusses how form that is new in the world is difficult to create. When a chemist creates a new salt he finds it difficult to obtain crystallisation. Scientists, however, persevere because the shape of the crystal is part of the definition of a new salt. It has been found that once a salt has been crystallised, it begins to be easier to crystallise again, even if subsequent crystallisations are in other laboratories. The explanation is not known within the realms of established physics.

Sheldrake[1] has come closest to giving a satisfactory answer when he explains that form for a new crystal does not yet exist. Once the salt has been persuaded to crystallise, then the form exists. Each time the salt is crystallised again, the form is strengthened, making it easier to bring form from the invisible to the visible world. The same thing has been noticed with inventions - almost the moment something is invented somebody else is inventing it somewhere else. Sheldrake[1] talks about how the more people come to hold an idea, the more other people will also. Thus the faster it will catch on. A woman in the audience asked if there was anyone else working on musical bowls. At the time I had not heard of anyone, but within a few days somebody told me that they had a friend in America, also working on the acoustic properties of turned form. He was, however, not experimenting with strings. He was turning wood from a musical background, pursuing visually harmonious forms and exploiting the acoustic properties they offered.

Another great influence has been Rudolf Steiner. He talks extensively about the nature of form. One example that Steiner[2] gives is the formation of plants. If you imagine a daffodil, the first thing you think of is the flower. If you think back from that point, you could imagine the bud - you could recognise a daffodil from its bud. Think back further and you will see green leaves with no bud. Some people can recognise daffodil leaves as distinct from tulip leaves - a gardener certainly could. Think back further, to winter, imagine taking the bulb in your hand. You may see that the bulb can be distinguished from a tulip bulb. The differences are not as great as the differences between flowers. From this exercise you may draw two conclusions. One, the form of the flower is more explicit than the form of the bulb. Two, the life cycle of the plant is a form in time - the movement from bulb to leaf to flower and back can be seen in the mind but not in space. Its existence as a time form is a reality that the mind can behold while the eye cannot.

This is an amazing example of a reality that is not sense-perceptible. Consider again. When a gardener holds a bulb in his hand, his mind is able to perceive the form of the flower. Where at that moment *is* the form of the flower? Now in your mind's eye again the bulb sprouts and the plant develops. The full form of the flowering plant is slowly appearing. Slowly the explicit form is moving out of the invisible realm into the visible. At the point of perfection, the form of the daffodil perceptible to you now in your mind's eye is visible to the physical eye. As the flower fades and dies, the form slips out of the sense-perceptible world again. The form is still there, your mind can perceive it at any moment, implicit in the bulb but not explicit in space. Matter grows to fill the form each spring, then falls out again toward summer. This is a clear example of form that is expressed in time and space. The theory of genes alone cannot explain this. The genes in a petal are identical to those in the stalk. Established science cannot explain why some cells form themselves into stalk or leaf and others into petal or root.

The life cycle of the daffodil is a form in time and the shape of the flower and the leaves at their fullest expression is a form in space. For me, the sounding bowls are an example of the same thing. The form in space is the completed bowl. Like the flowering plant, this is the fullest expression of a time-form. The time-form is the development from piano and poetry through wood turning to the sounding bowls and on through the music people make on them, and the experiences they gain. My ideal for these bowls is that, like the plants, they should serve their purpose as one of the more pleasant aspects of life.

References

1. Sheldrake R (1985). *A new science of life*. Grafton Books, London.

2. Steiner R (1987). Occult Science. Rudolph Steiner Press, London.

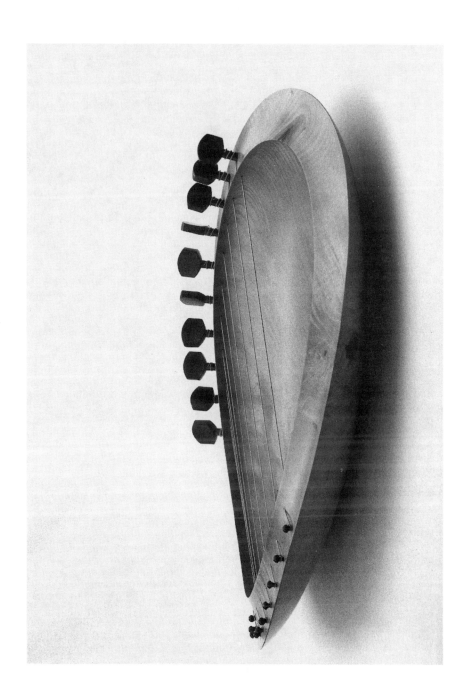

Why Work with the Dying?

Howard Delmonte
London, UK

This paper will examine and question some of the motivations of music therapists working in palliative and hospice care. Why work with the dying is a question that has been important for me to consider in my own work. However, I believe that it is not the answers that are important, but the journey of questioning.

About three years ago a friend was diagnosed with HIV. This news affected everyone related to him and directly or indirectly shaped all our lives. Once the shock settled and the implications of his diagnosis became reality we all began to try to make sense of his illness. We each reacted differently, changing various aspects of our lives: work/career changes, house purchases and relationship confrontations. In retrospect, what we seem to have been avoiding was the need to stay in the present (an extremely difficult achievement) and appreciate the *moment* as opposed to being stuck and trapped in the past or hypnotised by the future.

Dennis Potter,[1] a few months before he died of cancer, gave a moving and poignant interview where he illustrated this concept:

> *"We are the only animal that **knows** that we are going to die. The only thing that you know for sure is the present tense and that **nowness** becomes so vivid to me now, that almost in a perverse sort of way I am almost serene ... I can celebrate life. The **nowness** of everything is absolutely wondrous ... the fact that if you see the present tense, boy do you see it and boy can you celebrate it."*

It is this nowness that I believe music therapy can enable people to celebrate. Staying in the moment is a constant personal struggle as a music therapist. Words can distance me from my immediate feelings: 'How are you?', 'How are you feeling?'. These are phrases from our daily social repertoire. How often though,

109

have we felt frustrated, inadequate and occasionally redundant when attempting to answer?

A few months after my friend's diagnosis he decided to buy a piano. He had never taken music lessons but had a genuine love, belief and appreciation of the ability of music to touch the human soul and provide life with significance. It was truly beautiful to witness him exploring the piano through improvisation. It would appear that in the moment of music-making he was able to express and make sense of his life and feelings without words. The music may have enabled him to hear and feel his *nowness*.

I found myself exploring the idea of using music therapy in palliative and hospice care. After a meeting at St Catherine's Hospice and having given a presentation to staff, it was decided to go ahead with offering music therapy as part of the complementary therapies programme. I considered hypothetical questions; What would I expect to happen? How was I going to work? How would I cope? I began to realise that sessions and 'time' took on new meaning. Until now I had been aware of a music therapy process that facilitated and enabled a sense of change that was intensified and developed with time. Suddenly I was faced with a space that was heightened by 'endings' - indeed each session had its own sense of ending. Often I would only see a client once or twice before they died.

I believe these music therapy exchanges intensify the therapeutic relationship which in turn has an affect on me as therapist. In retrospect, they have, at times, opened more of my own personal boundaries and encouraged more of my own verbal disclosure. They have facilitated growth in *both* parties. During my initial period working in the hospice I was unable to understand the objective distance required that would help me see why I had chosen to work with the dying, or how my personal map had required that I take this significant journey into the unknown.

Later, I received a referral from a doctor, a client with advanced multiple sclerosis who was unable to speak. Initially, this client showed, through her facial expression, interest in only listening to my sounds on the flute and piano, often my musical response to being with her. During the fifth session I noticed how she looked at and acknowledged the piano, and subsequently asked if she would like to explore the instrument. She initially appeared keen, but within minutes of playing and stroking the keys (she had little strength in her fingers), she suddenly stopped and clearly indicated that she did not wish to continue. Her distorted voice seemed to express fear. This fear of musical expression continued to be an intense part of our work. Her non-musical participation became potent in our relationship, and this emphasised my music and my musical response to her situation. I became, or was made to be, her carrier and voice (the countertransference being extremely vital in this relationship). At times we sat in (painful) silence, other times I was compelled to 'play out' my countertransference feelings. Gradually the silences became less painful and more accepting.

Looking back, these sessions were musical expressions of being with a dying, often very angry person - about shared feelings of impotency and redundancy. At times I was extremely thankful for the language of sound to convey what otherwise would have been impossible to place into words. Each week I would check with her carer to see if she wanted to attend. I often hoped she would refuse. This client taught me about fear and unexpressed anger. She made me realise how inadequate words can be and how difficult it is for some terminally ill patients to accept their prognosis. Our sessions totalled eight. Each was like climbing an unknown mountain. I regularly asked myself what music therapy was offering her. After her death and with the support of my supervisor, I began to acknowledge the two-way process of our work; her silence, her pain, frustration and anger compelled me to respond and confront my fears and anxieties around death and dying.

This intense and exhausting exposure to the living-dying was the beginning of my questioning. By using the term *'living-dying'*, I refer to the importance that music therapy has in contacting and hearing the living and healthy part of the client as well as the failing and dying part. Here was a client whose struggle and painful conflicts of her decaying mind and body had forced me to acknowledge my own personal questions about my own mortality.

By listening to clients and my own questioning I have begun to realise that I may have unresolved questions about death which I want somehow to somehow explore consciously or unconsciously. As part of my music therapy training I was encouraged to listen to the client's needs. This means that it can be difficult at times to focus on my own. It may even be considered selfish or self-indulgent, yet they are there nonetheless. They may be apparent in my motives for the work I do. What are these motives? It is not my needs or motivations in themselves that are harmful, but their potential denial or avoidance. How many of us have witnessed professionals who use clients to fulfil their own wounded psyches; or who have an investment in 'their' clients staying emotionally or physically dependent? Jung[2] was right when he spoke of carers as 'wounded healers'.

111

Acknowledging why I am involved in palliative care, addressing my motives and needs, may help me to become of more value with my clients. In this way, I will hopefully not use clients *unconsciously* for my own ends, or force them to carry aspects of myself that I cannot face. What are these 'aspects' however, that I cannot confront or have postponed confronting?

Kübler-Ross[3] was once asked:
> *"You say be honest and share your gut reactions. Does this include saying I'm afraid of my feelings about death and haven't resolved them yet to a patient? Is it better to resolve them first and then talk to a patient?"*

Her answer was:
> *"Anyone who can admit and acknowledge that he is still afraid about his own feelings about death and has not resolved them and is comfortable enough to say so is not really petrified. As soon as the patient sees that you really care and that you too are human with human concerns, he will feel much more comfortable and will be much more able to share his own feelings."*

It is possible, therefore, that I am involved in my work with the dying because I recognise fundamental unresolved questions about death and dying. I am reminded of a friend who suggested that I must be brave to undertake such work. After some thought I replied that I was, myself, fearful of death and that perhaps I needed to try and make sense of that fear by facing it in my professional life.

People spend a great deal of time postponing pain and thoughts about impermanence and death. In Buddhist philosophy, death is a reality of life - by fully seeing death as a part of life Buddhists are enabled to appreciate life more. They eliminate clutter, and distracting thoughts by attempting to stay in the moment. Buddhists feel that if we believe in permanence then we will live life meaninglessly. To me that is a vital statement for it touches on a part of my work that I will return to - our search for *meaning* of life. Buddhism teaches that if you look into the meaning of death you will there find the meaning of life. In our culture the celebration of pregnancy and birth is intrinsic, yet death and dying is somehow rarely addressed until it arrives.

As a music therapist, when I am with near-death clients, I am often confronted with a mirror that may reflect my own death issues. One of the Buddhist meditations and reflections on death and dying is to imagine your own dying and death, attempting to see how you experience and feel it. It strikes me that when involved in working with the dying, witnessing all the daily achievements and struggles of the living-dying, I am in many ways facing this 'reflective' death on conscious or subconscious levels.

What silent and musical questions do patients living with AIDS confront me with? Recently a man with AIDS, whose partner was also at the advanced stage of the illness, turned to me toward the end of a session where he had acknowledged his fear of losing physical control, and said *"You must find your work difficult. How do you cope?"* Here again was a patient questioning *me* on many levels. Was he asking how I would cope with AIDS? How I feel about death? Or was he asking himself? By exposing myself to the living-dying, am I trying to cope with my own not-knowing? Or more probably, am I searching for *meaning*?

Within the music therapy relationship I believe there are moments of parallel quests for meaning. When working with the dying, the music therapy relationship is often intensified and may also become a collaborative process. Frankl[4] described how to make sense of our suffering - how this striving to find meaning in one's life is the primary motivational force in man. Civilisation is menaced because we are unable to find meaning in our lives - meaning that can transcend death and mortality, which the hustle of today's life denies. If we could find meaning and expression in our suffering then we would feel at ease in our daily lives. Frankl[4] states:

> *"For the meaning of life differs from man to man, from day to day and from hour to hour. What matters therefore is not the meaning in life in general, but rather the specific meaning of a person's life at a given moment."*

I feel that in 'critical moments'[5] music therapy may be able to provide an opportunity for clients to express and find meaning in their present life. If this force for meaning is real, then are we all searching for meaning? Could my participation and involvement in palliative care be part of my searching with sound and music for meaning? If there is a meaning in life, what meaning can there be in our clients' suffering? To try and answer this question I have once again to turn and listen with the client.

I was privileged to work with a lady (Mary) three months before she died. Towards the end of one of our sessions, and after a long silence, Mary looked up, smiled and vividly spoke out her thoughts. She described how she had never found

113

space for herself, because she had always been caring for her family and disturbed husband. She realised that her cancer had given her time to rest and be herself. I was aware that an important understanding had been shared. In that moment, Mary had been able to give her suffering meaning. Music therapy enabled her in some way, to validate her life and present existence. I believe this collaborative parallel quest for meaning affects both parties. When a client with a terminal illness asks: *"why, when I had so much left to do in my life, has this happened?"*, they are not necessarily looking for a direct answer. They may be vocalising an unconscious resentment at my apparently young and healthy life, or reflecting the very questions that I hold and struggle with in my daily work within the hospice.

When Mary acknowledged that through her illness she had found stillness and reflection I was silent, because I have often found myself contemplating this very question. That is, that some illnesses may be reproduced or psychosomatised for emotional and psychological reasons. Here was a human being of whom I had grown fond, who seemed to be mirroring my own thoughts. I felt paralysed as I realised the enormity of her statement and self-acknowledgement.

These momentary glimpses of patients' lives, whether musical or verbal, are extraordinary learning experiences and can be too easily taken for granted. Kübler-Ross[3] has stated:

> *"If we are willing to take an honest look at ourselves, hospice work can help us in our growth and maturity. No work is better suited for this than the dealing with very sick, old, or dying patients."*

Taking an honest look is difficult and requires self-monitoring that, at times, can be painful. Acknowledging my needs is vital if I am to be really present with my clients. Facing my own death, my own fear, hurt and distress as I participate in client's musical journeys is not easy, yet can be fruitful if acknowledged. When working with the living-dying it is inevitable as a human being that I will be exposed to and confronted by my own mortality. The visible and invisible questioning of clients will touch and penetrate my psyche and it is therefore important that I hear not only the questions of my clients, but also of myself. Gustav Mahler continually asked questions about death and dying in music and words:

> *"If I cannot find meaning in my life, I am confounded, I am faced with nothing but my nothingness."*[6]

As I have said, for many people live with dying, this is a crucial question - how can I give this life and suffering meaning?

Conclusion

'Why work with the dying', has been my question that has taken me on a journey. It is vital in my work as a music therapist that I am, at times, open to not knowing. Music therapy with the living-dying doesn't answer questions, it provides a space, a framework for both parties to question and feel. I have tried in this writing to question my motivations for working in palliative and hospice care and to address my unresolved feelings surrounding death. As Rousseau aptly said:

> *"He who pretends to look on death without fear, lies. All men are afraid of dying, this is the great law of sentient beings, without which the entire human species would soon be destroyed."*[5]

I am still learning and working with that fear.

References

1. Bragg M (July 1994). Channel IV interview with Dennis Potter.

2. Nouwen HJM (1982). *Wounded Healer*. Doubleday Image, USA.

3. Kübler-Ross E (1970). *On Death & Dying*. Routledge, London.

4. Frankl V (1959). *Man's Search for Meaning*. Washington Square Press, USA.

5. Lee C (1992). *The analysis of therapeutic improvisatory music with people living with HIV and AIDS*. Unpublished PhD Thesis, City University, London.

6. Holbrook D (1975). *Gustav Mahler and the Courage to Be*. Vision Press Ltd, London.

7. Rousseau JJ (1993). *Julie Or the New Eloise*. Bloomsbury, London.

Part Four

Guided Imagery and Music

Images of AIDS

Kenneth E Bruscia
Philadelphia, USA

This paper is based on two years of experience working with gay men living with AIDS. The method I used exclusively was Guided Imagery and Music (GIM) - an individual form of therapy in which the client images to music in a relaxed state while maintaining an ongoing dialogue with the therapist. Upon return to waking consciousness, the client reflects upon the GIM experience with the assistance of the therapist, either through verbal discussion or non-verbal means (e.g. mandalas or circle drawings). The discussions, relaxation inductions, starting image, taped music programs, and mandalas are all geared to help the client address therapeutic issues of greatest concern. A transcript is kept of each session. Advanced training is required to practice GIM, and especially when used for psychotherapeutic purposes.

From a psychotherapeutic point of view, PLWAs (People Living With AIDS) fall into three stages or categories:

- those who have tested positively to presence of the retrovirus in the blood, but have minor symptoms, if any

- those who have begun to experience more serious symptoms, but who do not have a life-threatening disease

- those who have a life-threatening disease. These stages are of psychological significance because of the different kinds of emotional issues that arise. As the possibility for denial decreases, the need for emotional healing or support increases.

In analyzing the imagery transcripts from over 150 GIM sessions, I have identified the following 'Images of AIDS' for gay men.

(1) **BEING IN LIMBO**: Some men reacted to the diagnosis by denying life. This was evidenced by a loss of career motivation, under-employment, boredom, flat affect, inactivity, procrastination, loss of pleasure, decrease in social life, etc. In the imagery, these men tended to stay in one place: being either stuck somewhere or unable to move. They would refuse to go through doors, enter rooms, or explore new places. They often came up against insurmountable walls. Colors within the images tended to be grey or lacking in lustre.

Others reacted by denying the disease and its prognosis. They tried to live in the fast lane, being as hedonistic as possible - as if the illness and death would never come. In the imagery, these men went everywhere and explored everything - but only on a superficial level. They would never linger, or stop long enough to check into their feelings. Their images and experiences were so vivid they were numbing! Colors were brilliant, blinding, overpowering.

Still others reacted by splitting themselves into conflicting parts or splitting themselves from the outside world. In the imagery, these men often found themselves in two places: as a character within the image or scene itself and as an observer watching from a distance; or as two different characters within the same image. Often the split would be between the self in the image and the self in the therapy room - these men avoided entering the imaginary realm without maintaining some kind of conscious control. When the split men were asked what an image felt like, they would have to rely upon the observer self; and they would rarely respond to invitations for the observer to 'step into' the image. Colors were black and white. In fact, a frequent occurrence was a sudden onset of images that were like 'photo negatives'.

A clinical example of living in limbo is Garrick's image of 'Eric', a sandman who was doomed to live in the narrow 'wet space' between the ocean waves and the dry sand on shore. Though his territory spread all the way down the eastern seaboard, Eric could not go near the ocean because the waves would smash him to pieces, and he could not go near the dry sand because the sun would dry him out and the wind would blow him away. More importantly, Eric was alone in the wet space - whenever anyone would try to love him by caressing or holding him, the part of his body touched would crumble.

(2) **RELEASING FEELINGS**: Once out of 'limbo', intense feelings often surface. Each man seemed to struggle with one central emotion in particular,

with various others constellated around it. The emotion most commonly shared by these men was guilt or shame; other significant ones were anger, loneliness, fear and grief.

Feelings of guilt were evident in images of the self as mutilated, emaciated or very small. Many men linked these feelings to AIDS through images of blood. Men with guilt feelings would also try to please me, and always have a 'good' session.

A clinical example is the story of the set of bones that one man found and reconstructed in his imagery. The bones belonged to a man who was being stoned to death by an unaccepting, angry crowd. The imager kept shifting between the man being stoned and the people stoning him. The session concluded with him burying the man, and with blood left on his hands, realizing: 'I must forgive myself'.

Another example is the man who relived an explosion he narrowly avoided in real life. Upon returning to the scene, he chose to stay there instead of escaping, and was therefore blown up into little pieces. His best friend (who was heterosexual) picked up his bloodied head and began to carry it to a safe place. As the imager felt his friend's hands gently caressing his head, he revealed his secret gay life and was forgiven by his friend. The symbolism within this image is very multifaceted.

Feelings of anger have been manifested in pounding, screaming, and bouts of furious cursing - at God, parents, lovers, friends and self. In the images, men who were angry saw blood on other people. They were also suspicious or critical of the music and me. Unexpressed anger was manifested through body armor, inappropriate and constant humor, and images of storing or holding back very powerful forces (e.g. ocean walls). I found that anger was frequently linked to grief.

Feelings of loneliness were obvious, when session after session, the imager would be alone in his imagery, never coming across another human being, never being touched, held or loved. Music with long solo melodies or very desolate harmonic structures would frequently cause deep crying, and a need to be held. Loneliness was frequently accompanied by shame and grief.

Feelings of fear were expressed through avoidance of deep, altered states, or images of oneself in terrifying circumstances or extreme physical danger (e.g. being eaten alive, or being burned). These men would often find themselves ungrounded, falling backwards through dark spaces, or gasping for air. They also tended to ruminate over their bodies and inspect themselves frequently for any signs of Karposi's sarcoma - the most dreaded symptom. Feelings of grief were manifested through body armor and images of loss, and were often released in deep crying, wordless images, or images of reunion. Unlike any other disease, AIDS strikes not only the individual gay man, but also his entire support system. It is the disease of multiple losses: first friends - dropping one at a time - and then oneself. Grieving is very difficult, for many men fear that once they start they will not be able to stop. It is as if they are holding back tears from an ocean of sorrow.

(3) *FINDING LOVE*:   The most striking imagery experience - the only one found in nearly every case - has been a reunion with a loved one who had died.   Deceased parents, grandparents, siblings, friends, and lovers would spontaneously appear in the images to console, guide, reassure or simply visit with the imager. Whenever this happened, emotional healing of some kind would invariably take place.

An example given is the imager who saw himself as an emaciated person from Bangladesh, waiting on his living room sofa for his beloved 'Granny' to rescue him. Sitting there, he cried and cried, fearing that she had abandoned him because he was gay and had AIDS. In a later session, after he had resolved the contempt he had for his parents, Granny came to him and embraced him, scolding him humorously - *"How could you think I would not love you just the same?"*

(4) *EMOTIONAL HEALING*: Emotional healing experiences took place either during the visit with the deceased loved one, or afterwards, in later images or sessions. Those who felt guilty found redemption; those who were angry found forgiveness; those who were alone found loving support; those who were anxious found courage and strength; and those who were grieving found comfort.

(5) *EMBRACING LIFE AND DEATH*: As emotions were healed, the men were able to start living again - not in limbo, not with the same pent-up feelings, but with a love inside that could carry them forward. They no longer had to live as if they were dead, but could start to live more fully until it was their time to die. Those who were ready embraced death as willingly as life.

What becomes obvious in every clinical example is that the five themes I have identified are woven together quite closely. Each man constellated the five themes and worked through them in his own unique way. The process was not always as sequential as implied. Some men had to release feelings before they could find love; others had to find love before they could release feelings. It should also be noted that not every man was ready for embracing life and death, but chose to stay in limbo.

I found that GIM was particularly well-suited for working with the issues involved in living with AIDS. This does not mean that it solved every problem, or that it provided emotional relief for everyone. Much depended upon the maturity of the client, his ability to work through old emotional wounds from childhood, and his spiritual readiness for self-healing. These variables, in turn, often depended upon where the man was in the course of the disease. Those in the earlier stages were often less ready to do the in-depth work that men in later stages were.

The intensity of this work has taught me the importance of taking care of myself as a therapist. In order to truly be there for someone in such terrible emotional pain, a therapist has to be strong and steady, yet able to resonate. This is especially critical in GIM because the therapist experiences the images and the music with the client. Entering the client's emotional world is sometimes quite frightening and overpowering. Sometimes the pain is almost unbearable.

Good health is essential, along with hope and humor. When we lose any of these, we must give ourselves permission to rest. Often, we need our own therapy! And so I encourage every music therapist to drink deeply of our own source of wellness - MUSIC.

A Journey of Transition
with Guided Imagery and Music

Denise Erdonmez
Victoria, Australia

This paper will describe a series of five Guided Imagery and Music sessions with a 50-year-old woman with Motor Neurone Disease (MND). Her ability to engage music and imagery enabled her to face images of death and transition and experience profound spiritual growth.

Motor Neurone Disease (also known as amyotrophic lateral sclerosis - ALS) is characterised 'by a progressive degeneration of the ... spinal cord causing motor neurone lesions'.[1] Lower motor neurone lesions result in flaccidity and upper lesions result in spasticity. MND differs from other neurological diseases in that the person may be cognitively intact with no mental deterioration. However, speech may be significantly impaired due to muscle weakness and spasticity, resulting in dysarthria and dysphagia. MND most commonly occurs between the ages of 50-70 and the mean duration of survival is only three years. The prevalence is approximately five per 100,000.

Guided Imagery and Music (GIM)

GIM, devised by Helen Bonny[2,3] is a method of music therapy in which classical music is used to evoke and stimulate imagery, so that self-exploration and personal growth can occur. GIM involves a relationship between therapist and client over a number (series) of sessions. Typically, each GIM session lasts one-and-a-half to two hours and involves a pre-music discussion in which therapist and client clarify the issue of focus. An individually tailored relaxation induction is given, the client moving, with eyes closed, into a deeply relaxed state. At the end of the induction a focus is given to bridge the relaxation with the music and flow of imagery.

The therapist chooses a tape of approximately 30-40 minutes duration, from a library of 26 tapes especially programmed by Helen Bonny. The client listens to the music and is encouraged to share images, impressions, fantasies, and/or feelings as they occur in response to the music. The therapist makes a written transcript of the imagery and encourages the experience through appropriate interventions. These interventions may be supportive, seek clarification, or allow the client to hold an image or feeling for a period long enough to experience it fully. At the end of the tape, the therapist brings the client back from the deeply relaxed state to an alert state. The content of the imagery session is then processed by relating and integrating the imagery into aspects of the person's daily life. This is achieved either by talking through the experience or by free drawing.

GIM is closely aligned to Jungian philosophy and analytic psychology where personal issues are identified, explored and resolved through the use of symbolic images, shapes and forms. In GIM, early-life memories may emerge, and repressed emotions be brought to the surface. GIM allows these memories and emotions to be explored, bringing about new insights, resolution of conflicts and healing.

Not all clients are suited to GIM. Wylie and Blom[4] have adapted GIM for hospice patients, using country and western music in one case and light classical music in another. The clients reported that GIM gave relief from pain. Martin, in an unpublished paper,[5] explores the contradictions of GIM with the terminally ill. She describes her belief that GIM is largely inappropriate for people experiencing pain because it requires energy to engage the imagery, and because the imagery evokes psychological issues. Martin concludes that in advanced stages of disease people often do not resolve major life issues and need to be comfortable, not challenged.

Bruscia[6] describes the process of GIM for a man with AIDS, in which significant images recurred throughout the series. GIM is a powerful medium to address the multiple layers of grieving which occur for those with AIDS.[7]

Imagery and Visualisation in Disease

GIM is one of a number of imagery or visualisation techniques used to help people in spiritual and psychological growth. Research has shown that imagery and visualisation techniques help stimulate the human immune system to combat disease and help people have control over their experience of pain. Simonton, Simonton and Creighton[8] devised a technique for people undergoing chemotherapy that enables them to visualise cancer cells as weak and confused. The person then visualises the healthy tissue as powerful and strong, capable of destroying the cancer cells. Achterberg[9] utilises imagery and visualisation to identify diseased areas of the body and so facilitate diagnosis and treatment.

126

In her book 'Imagery in Healing', Achterberg[9] outlines three aspects of imagery in disease, illness and recovery:

- She argues that a person's experience of disease and illness is influenced strongly by images. A diagnosis of cancer, for instance, evokes images for the patient - of pain, surgery and ultimate death. Imagery, therefore, is already part of the process of disease and illness.

- Achterberg illustrates the use of imagery in assisting diagnosis and prognosis of physical illness. She works with patients to rehearse imagery techniques; to imagine the diseased cells fighting the healthy white blood cells.

- Imagery is used as therapy - to identify problem areas, to explore blocks and resistance, to give expression to resentments and sadness, and to allow for growth and healing.

In discussing client's images, Achterberg evaluates three aspects:

- the disease imagery is assessed for vividness of image, its strength (or weakness) and ability to persist

- the treatment imagery is examined for vividness and effectiveness of the mechanism for cure

- the imagery for personal defenses is evaluated in terms of the vividness of description and action.

Achterberg found that images most often associated with good prognoses were Archetypal figures, protectors of the people, such as Arthur and his Knights, the venturesome Vikings, and power animals such as the wolf, bear and lion.
Poor prognoses were associated with:

- amorphous images for the immune system (such as snowflakes or clouds)

- images of immutable objects for the cancer cells (such as lumps of coal or submarines)

In the following case study, GIM was used to help a woman facing the terminal stages of disease. The imagery she experienced can be closely interpreted in relation to the progression of her disease. More importantly, her spiritual growth was profound and exemplifies the power of music and imagery to expand a person's view of life and its meaning.

Case Study - Mary

Introduction

Mary was a 50-year-old woman who had five GIM sessions over a period of 15 months. During this time she lived with the relentless progression of Motor Neurone Disease. The case study illustrates how Mary accepted death at a subconscious level, while maintaining denial at the conscious level.

Kubler-Ross[10] described how society perpetuates our fear of death and that as a result people need to defend themselves psychologically from fear. One defence mechanism used is that of denial. Kubler-Ross believes denial is a healthy way of dealing with uncomfortable and painful situations. It is a buffer against shocking news, and allows the patient time and psychological space to collect him/herself and, with time, accept the prognosis of the terminal nature of his/her disease.

Denial is usually a temporary defense, although if maintained throughout an illness may culminate in increased stress and anxiety. People with strong religious beliefs may stay in a state of denial, believing that if their faith in God is strong enough they will get better. There is mounting evidence of some patients being able to do exactly that. With an increase in the positive outcome of some diseases, remissions do occur.[11] Therapists, therefore, need to be wary of a judgemental attitude to the patient 'in denial' in that they may well succeed in controlling, or slowing down the progression of the disease.

Mary remained in denial until the last stages of her life, finally admitting that she 'wasn't going to make it'. Her imagery in GIM sessions, however, showed that she was preparing herself, at an inner level, for death.

Background

Mary was the oldest child of a family of four, and the only girl. She trained as a social worker and spent 25 years in Asia with a religious

128

organisation. She made infrequent visits home to Australia, these increasing when her father became ill and was diagnosed with MND. When he was in the terminal stage of the disease, Mary visited home, returning to Asia just prior to his death. She carried guilt that she had returned to Asia instead of staying with her father and being present when he died.

Six months after the father's death, Mary developed the first symptoms of MND - weakness of the leg muscles. She attempted many cures in Asia including acupuncture, herbal remedies and the spiritual laying on of hands. She had received a series of verbal Guided Imagery sessions (without music) with a spiritual healer, and she had found these helpful. In the Guided Imagery sessions she travelled on a path, the process being related to the therapist verbally, just as in GIM. When Mary approached me for GIM sessions she was already experienced in relating images, and thus immediately engaged the GIM process.

The GIM sessions were given in her home. At this stage both legs were weak and she crawled on all fours, dragging her legs behind her. She denied she had the symptoms of MND and in fact, the medical tests had not yet shown positive. She was able to discuss the major aspects of her life and her disappointments. She responded well to the relaxation induction and quickly engaged the imagery process as the music began. The tape for the first session comprised music from the Impressionist period - the Dances Sacred and Profane and the Prelude a l'apres midi d'un faune, both by Debussy; Venus from Holst's Planets Suite and Vaughan Williams' Fantasia on 'Greensleeves'.

Mary's imagery in the first session showed repeated frustration with mobility. She was on a path, but the roots of the trees blocked her walking. She began to climb a staircase inside a large house. The staircase kept elongating so that she could not get to the top. Later she was confronted by two large mountains and there was no path around them. Mary's imagery in this session also depicted many disappointments. The large house she was in was deserted. When she finally reached the top of the staircase, she stepped onto a mountain which was desolate, and then it deflated. In the discussion that followed, Mary indicated that she wanted to work on several issues, unresolved grief for her father's death, 'loss of productivity' and disappointments in her work in Asia.

129

The music for the second session comprised of six pieces that were contrasting in style and mood. In the first piece (an excerpt from Ravel's Daphnis and Chloe) she explored a river. The water was a murky brown, and the mud came half-way up her legs. She was walking in a stream, but the river (of life) dried up and she was left in sand (insecure). She then explored a forest where the trees were close and uniform in shape. This may represent the rigidity of her life, and her striving for perfection. She came to a wooden door. It was made of coarse wood, and there were nails in the wood (an image of the coffin or of the crucifixion). She knocked on the door and it opened stiffly. She explored the other side of the door and found dense fog. She had a choice of following a yellow light up through the fog, or sitting on top of the trees of the forest. She chose the trees, which she said 'have prepared a special place for me'.

This imagery suggests that she was beginning to prepare herself at an inner level for death: '..a special place with the trees'.

Session three took place six months later, as she had been away in the North of Australia. Mary was now wheelchair-bound and needed assistance with toileting, dressing and feeding. Her speech was slow and laboured and she showed difficulty in swallowing. Despite these difficulties she was able slowly to articulate the imagery experiences in an audible voice.

During the relaxation induction I suggested she take the image of an object on her journey. She chose an amethyst stone. I chose music that was strong and powerful - the tape entitled Mostly Bach. The music included fugues, a passacaglia, a sarabande (orchestral arrangements taken from keyboard compositions) and the slow movement of Bach's concerto for two violins in D minor. The texture of the music was mostly contrapuntal with rich harmonies and strong rhythms.

In her imagery, she moved toward a tunnel (associated with birthing imagery). It was thick and deceptive - it looked like it was comfortable but she said "*it doesn't have good intentions*". She crawled through the tunnel and came out into something white and cold - it was dead coral. She felt like a tortoise (Cirlot[12] described the tortoise as the oldest symbol for Mother Earth). She was very uncertain. The tortoise came out of the water and was dried out in the sun. It became a skeleton, and its claws tried to dig into the earth to find the amethyst. Then she encountered a wise old man. Mary described his face, but then the face became a mask and she felt let down. She became a bird, flapped her wings. She wanted to move on but her legs were caught in a cloud. She spoke with the cloud and asked it to let go of her legs. The cloud gave an ultimatum that it would let her go if she left one leg behind. The cloud mocked her. Another cloud appeared and negotiated on her behalf. The second cloud required that Mary trust it: 'you may not be able to understand what is happening but just trust'. The first cloud then shrivelled up and both her legs are freed. The cloud put her back on earth and she scratched (still as a bird) in the ground for the amethyst. She found the original stone, and said 'your rightful place is buried in the earth'. She put the amethyst back in the earth so that 'everybody has it'.

The symbolism of this imagery was clearly evident, in that the disease had already affected both her legs. Achterberg's assessment of images also applied here; she imaged the illness as amorphous (i.e. as clouds). A further development of her spiritual growth was seen in the message of trust: 'you may not understand what is happening, but just trust', and later 'your rightful place is in the earth'.

In session four Mary was confronted by an old woman in a dark cloak (this was the 'old hag' archetype, or wise woman, crone, the negative mother). Mary called to the old woman and they sat together on the sand. Suddenly the old woman was gone and in her place a striped brightly coloured snake appeared. (The snake can be representative of deception or sexuality or healing). Mary became a big insect, and crawled up a rocky mountain. She lost energy, but was unable to give herself a rest. She was helped by a fluffy brown cat, who suggested she levitate. She became an eagle which confronted a black cloud. She batted her wings at the cloud, which finally retreated. In this imagery of the cloud, Mary confronted the cloud herself, whereas in the earlier session she needed the second cloud to negotiate on her behalf. This session indicated a strength in confronting the disease and gaining some sense of control over it.

In the fifth and final session, Mary's imagery indicated that at a subconscious level she was preparing for death. At the conscious level however, she was still in denial. She said about her deteriorating speech; *"don't tell Mum, she'll only worry"*. Her mother, of course, was well aware of her daughter's deteriorating condition. I chose the tape entitled 'Transitions' for this session. The music started out as strong, masculine in quality and provided a secure background for the work (Richard Strauss: 'Ein Heldenleben'). The final piece was the slow movement of Brahms' Second Piano Concerto in Bb major. The closing music was slow and lyrical in quality, interweaving between solo cello and piano.

Mary's imagery commenced under a Banyan tree (which characteristically has large roots visible above the earth). Under the roots was an egg. She didn't know whether to open it, bury it, or take it with her. She decided to meditate about the egg, and a crack soon appeared. Inside the egg was another hard shell - a seed. Again she was unsure whether to open the seed or bury it. I asked if she could see inside the seed - *"yes!"* she said, *"I am lying down, I've gone to sleep. The seed is sprouting green shoots, to start a mini forest"* (the Brahms Piano Concerto slow movement commences here). *"This beautiful thing inside me - this is my life. My place is to put the seed in the earth - I've found what I was looking for - I can leave it in peace knowing that it will fulfil itself - one day I will return. I feel a warm light mist over me - now I've disappeared"*.

I was moved by the significance of those images: those indicating a preparation for death - she lies down to sleep - she can leave in peace knowing the seed will fulfil itself - one day she will return, and also the richness of her language - 'this beautiful thing inside me ...' spoken very slowly but with great meaning. At the end of the session, Mary said *"that's the end, a good finale"*.

In processing the imagery, I asked what seemed the most important image - she responded *"discovering that the essence of truth was within the seed itself"*. I asked what was the significance of the seed, to which she replied *"the idea of self-healing - the essence of healing within yourself, free of the physical body - I felt fulfilled - thought I would come back in a transformed state one day - I've done what I was supposed to do."* I asked if she felt her work here was finished, to which she said *"you can only live one day at a time"*.

Mary again went North in search of the sun. On her return she was frail and weak, she was admitted to hospital and died soon after. It was eight weeks after her last GIM session.

Conclusion

Over the five sessions, Mary addressed a number of issues relating to her life. She confronted the shadow (the disease), which appeared twice in the shape of a cloud. She met archetypal figures on her journeys - the wise old man (whose face became a mask), the old hag (who transformed into a snake), and tortoise (symbol of Earth Mother).

Deeper work happened at the inner level. Through the imagery, she symbolically worked through the meaningfulness of her life and experienced it as feeling 'fulfilled'. The imagery also indicated a belief in an after life, in a transformed state. At this deep inner level she had prepared herself for death. At the outer level she needed to travel to the warmth of the sun before allowing the physical body to separate and die.

It was interesting that Mary was able to use GIM despite her difficulties with speech. Although her rate of speech slowed down considerably, and articulating words was difficult, Mary was, nevertheless, able to articulate her imagery experiences. This was all the more significant when the quality of her language is appreciated. In her last session, the words used to describe the imagery experiences were rich in meaning, and showed a state of mind connected to the meaning of her life. It was also evident that there was no cognitive impairment.

The process for Mary then, was her own journey, an inner journey or preparation for the final act of individuation - separation from the living world. That her last GIM session gave her a sense of fulfilment - of having done in her life what she came to do - was a testimony to the profound inner experience of GIM.

References

1. Oliver DJ, O'Gorman B & Saunders C (1986). Motor Neurone Disease. In: Downie P (ed), *Cash's Textbook of Neurology for Physiotherapists*. London, Faber and Faber.

2. Bonny H (1978a). *Facilitating Guided Imagery and Music Sessions. Monograph No 1*. Salina KS: Bonny Foundation.

3. Bonny H (1978b). *The Role of Taped Music Programs in the GIM Process. Monograph No 2*. Salina KS: Bonny Foundation.

4. Wylie ME & Blom R (1986). Guided Imagery and Music with Hospice Patients. *Music Therapy Perspectives*; *3*: 25-28.

5. Martin (1992). *An exploration of the Contraindications in the Bonny method of Guided Imagery and Music with the Terminally Ill.* Unpublished paper, New York University.

6. Bruscia K (1991). Embracing life with AIDS: Psychotherapy through Guided Imagery and Music (GIM). In Bruscia K (ed), *Case Studies in Music Therapy.* Phoenixville, PA: Barcelona Press.

7. Bruscia K (1992). Visits from the other side: Healing persons with AIDS through Guided Imagery and Music (GIM). In Campbell D (ed), *Music and Miracles.* Wheaton IL: Quest Books.

8. Simonton OC, Simonton S & Creighton J (1980). *Getting well again.* New York, Bantam.

9. Achterberg J (1985). *Imagery in Healing.* Boston, New Science Library.

10. Kubler-Ross E (1969). *On death and dying.* New York, Macmillan.

11. Siegel B (1986). *Love, Medicine and Miracles.* London, Rider.

12. Cirlot (1971). *A Dictionary of Symbols.* London, Routledge.

Part Five

Collaboration

Therapeutic Touch in Palliative Care Music Therapy

Mary Rykov
Toronto, Canada

Introduction

I was skeptical of therapeutic touch until I experienced it for myself. Learning and developing over the years I have found it to be like my experience of music: there is no end for potential growth - it is continually evolving and changing. I initially kept my practice of therapeutic touch and music therapy separate. Over time however, they converged. For example, I found myself using aspects of therapeutic touch to facilitate vocal work with a head-injury client, and alternating sessions of therapeutic touch and music therapy with a client recovering from post-traumatic stress disorder. It was when I started working more intensively in the area of palliative care music therapy that I felt a clear need for therapeutic touch because of its ability to ease the dying process.[5,13]

My first presentation of therapeutic touch[32] included parallels with music therapy. The presentation at this conference pertained specifically to the practice of palliative care at the bedside of patients who are at the end-stage of terminal illnesses. This paper will define therapeutic touch, its theoretical framework, and basic assumptions. Therapeutic touch indications, phases, and outcomes will be described; details of the Conference demonstration will be omitted.

I will identify four ways that therapeutic touch interfaces with music therapy. I will discuss its value as a knowledge base in palliative care practice and in therapist self-care. Therapeutic touch is a useful technique in palliative care music therapy that has become essential to my practice.

Definition and Description

Therapeutic touch is defined as being a contemporary interpretation of several ancient healing practices that entails 'a consciously directed process of energy exchange during which the practitioner uses the hands as a focus to facilitate healing'.[26] The term, 'therapeutic touch' was developed by Krieger[14,15,16] in 1972 to describe the method of healing by energy transfer taught to her by the healer Dora Kunz.[19,10] Krieger, professor emerita of New York University, researched and taught therapeutic touch to graduate nursing students, and to others outside the university.

Therapeutic touch assumes the capacity for healing is innate; it is a human skill that can be taught and learned.[14,15,6,22] Therapeutic touch assumes human beings are open, complex, and pandimensional energy systems through which, in health, energy flows in a balanced, symmetrical manner.[19] During states of disease and stress, energy is unbalanced, congested, and blocked; the normal flow is disrupted.

The framework underlying these assumptions is the force field derivative of systems theory.[12,4,35,37] Fundamental to the practice of therapeutic touch is the theoretical framework of human multidimensional anatomy,[6,20,7,10,18] including chakra centres and the energy field extending beyond the physical body boundary. Therapeutic touch is consistent with Eastern philosophies (e.g. Hinduism, Buddhism) and the Western philosophical school of vitalism. Vitalism posits that the phenomenon of life cannot be explained in material terms alone.

Indications for therapeutic touch are to enhance rapport, relieve pain, decrease anxiety, accelerate healing (where appropriate), and/or promote a sense of well-being. Research exploring therapeutic touch has addressed anxiety,[8,30] increased hemoglobin levels,[16] childbirth,[15,9,1] pain,[23,24,36,21] tension headaches,[11] wound healing,[33,34] and immunity.[29] The most reliable outcomes of therapeutic touch are a rapid relaxation response, amelioration or eradication of pain, and facilitation of healing processes (e.g. of wounds or fractures).[14] Therapeutic touch does not normally exceed a duration of 30 minutes. Treatment for infants, children, pregnant women, people with psychiatric disorders, the elderly, and those who are ill or debilitated is shorter due to their increased sensitivity.

Therapeutic touch consists of a number of phases following an initial meditative centring focused by a compassionate intent to help. The energy field beyond the physical body is then scanned and assessed. Disturbances found in the field are cleared; this is also known as 'unruffling', 'smoothing' or 'preparing the field' for treatment. Treatment occurs through modulation and transfer of energy directed through the practitioner to the client. The energetic field is rebalanced ·q methods specific to the cues that have been perceived. The process is ˑted by stabilizing the energy flow in the field. Centring is always the ˑntal first phase. Subsequent phases may be intermingled and/or ˑus.

Therapeutic touch is not a medical cure; it concerns energy balance and flow rather than medical diagnoses. Therapeutic touch is derived from the 'laying on of hands' but it is not a miracle or faith cure; it is not dependent on religious belief or placebo effects. Krieger[16] describes it as 'a primitive, simple (that is, direct), and elegant use of human energies in the service of a humane act. It is from compassion that it draws its power'. Janet Macrae[22] relates a poignant example of its completeness while she was treating a little boy in hospital who was dying of cancer:

> The child's grandfather, who spoke very little English, would visit sometimes, but as it was so difficult for him to see the boy in this condition, he would usually withdraw and sit looking out the window. As soon as I started to use therapeutic touch, however, the grandfather came immediately to the bedside and joined me in the practice. He knew exactly what to do and we worked together, beautifully synchronized, in silence. When I felt that the boy had had enough, I looked at his grandfather: our eyes met, he nodded and then went back to the window. I knew then that therapeutic touch is a mode of communication in its own right. It is the same art the world over, needing, like music, no interpretation.

Therapeutic Touch in Practice

Therapeutic touch combines with my practice of palliative care music therapy in four ways. First, through my own centring, secondly as symptom control, thirdly as something the family can be taught, and finally - but not least - as manifested energetically through the music.

Centring

Therapeutic touch requires meditative centring. It is from a place deep within that the practitioner interacts with the client. This requires stepping outside of usual consciousness to connect with the realm of pure being and intuition. Before making music at a bedside I centre just as I do before starting therapeutic touch. This may take place quickly - even instantaneously - but it is always on a conscious level. Centring enhances music therapy experience by enabling me to 'be' present from a depth within myself that is beyond the roles of 'therapist' and 'patient', beyond even the illusions of living and dying. It enables acute listening that is beyond sound.

Symptom Control

Therapeutic touch interfaces with music therapy for symptom control because it can relieve pain. It enabled me to offer music therapy to a home hospice patient who was otherwise too uncomfortable to engage. Her face was contorted with pain and her breathing jagged. She cried out to me, 'No, no, not today. No music today. I can't, I can't. No singing today. This pain is bad, oh God, oh God. It hurts too bad.' I asked her where it hurt, and she pointed to the right lower side of her abdomen. I placed my hand above the spot and felt a disturbance in the field. It felt like a thick block of pressure that Janet Macrae[22] describes as 'loose congestion'. Using a technique described by Chiappone[3] as 'siphoning', I drew the sensation of the 'block' in her field out through the palm of my left hand; I was aware of it travelling up my left arm, across my shoulders, down my right arm, and out the palm of my right hand. When the disturbance was gone her face softened. She shuddered a sigh of relief and lay back silently on her pillows, breathing deeply. I then received permission to play music for her, and sang the song she requested. She was soon sleeping peacefully. Without initial therapeutic touch, music therapy would not have been possible.

Teaching Families

Therapeutic touch can be taught to family members. Palliative care philosophy views the whole family as the unit of care; therefore, they can be the object of our interventions when appropriate. I have, on occasion, given therapeutic touch to the patient and all other family members present, explaining and teaching as I worked. Family members express appreciation for the deep relaxation they experience, as well as appreciation for having something concrete they can learn also. This diminishes the sense of helplessness so often experienced in the face of a loved one's progressive disease and discomfort.

Music

Finally, therapeutic touch interfaces with palliative care music therapy, generally, through the music. Music is physical and touches us. I am acutely aware of this physical touch as I project music, consciously directing and modulating the energy that carries the sound, just as I modulate energy during therapeutic touch treatment. I sense for reactions in the field and adjust my sound and energy accordingly. I therefore practise therapeutic touch through music, rather than my hands.

Therapeutic touch, in turn, adds another dimension to my experience of playing and listening. Live music is enhanced when music is worked with energetically.

Therapeutic Touch in Palliative Care as a Knowledge Base

In addition to the music improvisational techniques and theories indigenous to training,[25,27,28,2] music therapists incorporate numerous techniques and theories from other disciplines that become integral to their work. Family systems theory, analytical theory, developmental theory, group dynamics theory, and verbal counselling skills are examples. I posit that the theory and technique of therapeutic touch is a useful extra-music therapy knowledge base for music therapists working in palliative care.

Therapeutic touch and its energy field theory of human multidimensional anatomy is a knowledge base that offers a world view different from Western clinical anatomy and allopathic medicine. A multiplicity of world views has always existed. The more perspectives, the richer the view.

Therapeutic touch is useful for all health care professionals working in palliative care because of its capacity to alleviate suffering for patients and families. If the mandate of palliative care is to provide comfort and increase quality of life, then music therapists must be willing to be flexible in accommodating clients' needs. This will entail extra-musical skills. Therapeutic touch is an extra-musical skill that can make a significant contribution.

Therapeutic Touch as Self-Care for the Music Therapist

Working in palliative care is painful. The pain may stem from countertransference, from witnessing multiple deaths, or from the experience of unresolved grief. Therapeutic touch is my care-giver because it facilitates working through hurt and enables me to integrate the experience of dying. Therapeutic touch functions as self-care because it is a secular, spiritual practice. Spiritual groundedness is crucial to my well-being and my work. It is a human meta-need similar to experiencing beauty and aesthetic expression.

Therapeutic touch is soul work. It is a meditative process that affords an interior attitude that is a being-in-harmony with the greater influences of nature.[17] It is focused withdrawal from the world of reaction inward to the heart, listening to the soul. Therapeutic touch entails interaction that taps this reservoir of peace, projecting it outward.

Centring and meditation in therapeutic touch also acknowledges a letting-go-of-outcome. The practitioner does not 'do' or 'cause' healing; nor does he/she use personal energies in the process, but serves as a channel for vital energy. The therapeutic touch practitioner is an 'instrument' for healing. The rebalancing of the energy field facilitates the healee's own processes. This may result in health or death. This letting-go-of-outcome is congruent with my philosophy as a professional and serves to remind me not to be judgmental or divest energy in music therapy outcomes.

This inner dimension of consciousness is a great source of healing. It mitigates hurt by maintaining contact with the greater influences, the implicate order of Nature. Meditation cultivates soul and enables greater depths of being with oneself and others. It is this cultivation of soul that has become crucial to my work and life.

Conclusion

Therapeutic touch is not an intellectual exercise. It is more than just another technique, another 'bag of tricks'. It is profound lived experience. Therapeutic touch is a healing skill that can be learned by anyone. It is understandable, however, that not everyone might choose to learn. I was indeed skeptical when first introduced to it and cautious about using it in my work. Now it is as necessary and natural to me as music.

Therapeutic touch is a valuable extra-musical skill that is congruent with the principles and practice of music therapy in palliative care. It has the capacity for increasing the quality of life for patients, families, and music therapists. I hope all who read this work will gain understanding and appreciation of the potential for therapeutic touch and its possible contribution to music therapy. Perhaps some readers will be curious enough to experience it directly.

References

1. Fanslow-Brunjes CA (1991). Healing of the dying. Bereavement. Workshops conducted in Toronto, April 1991.

    ieger D (1994). The healing moment that lives. Keynote address to the
    n Mountain Oncology Group and the Rutland Medical Center, Rutland,
    nt, September 30, 1994.

3. Rykov M (1992). *A music therapy introduction to therapeutic touch.* Proceedings of the Nineteenth Annual Conference of the Canadian Association for Music Therapy, 133-136.

4. Nurse Healers-Professional Associates (1992). *Therapeutic touch teaching guidelines: Beginner level Krieger/Kunz method.* New York: Nurse Healers-Professional Associates, Inc. Cooperative.

5. Krieger D (1993). *Accepting your power to heal: The personal practice of therapeutic touch.* Sante Fe, NM: Bear & Company.

6. Krieger D (1987). *Living the therapeutic touch: Healing as a lifestyle.* New York: Dodd, Mead & Company

7. Krieger D (1979). *The therapeutic touch: How to use your hands to help or heal.* Englewood Cliffs, NJ: Prentice-Hall, Inc.

8. Kunz D (Ed) (1985). *Spiritual aspects of the healing arts.* Wheaton, IL: The Theosophical Publishing House.

9. Karagula S & Kunz D (1989). *The chakras and the human energy fields.* Wheaton, IL: The Theosophical Publishing House.

10. Gerber (1988). *Vibrational medicine: New choices for healing ourselves.* Sante Fe, NM: Bear & Company.

11. Macrae J (1988). *Therapeutic touch: A practical guide.* New York: Alfred A. Knopf.

12. Kenny CB (1989). *The field of play: A guide for the theory and practice of music therapy.* Atascadero, CA: Ridgeview Publishing Company.

13. Eagle CT (1991). Steps to a theory of quantum therapy. *Music Therapy Perspectives*; *9*: 56-60.

14. Wolf FA (1989). *Taking the quantum leap: The new physics for non-scientists.* New York: Harper & Row, Publishers.

15. Zukav G (1979). *The dancing wu li masters: An overview of the new physics.* New York: Bantam Books.

16. Leadbeater CW (1927). *The chakras.* Wheaton, IL: Theosophical Publishing House.

17. Grey A (1990). *Sacred mirrors: The visionary art of Alex Grey*. Rochester, VT: Inner Traditions International.

18. Kunz D (1991). *The personal aura*. Wheaton, IL: The Theosophical Publishing House.

19. Heidt P (1981). Effect of therapeutic touch on the anxiety level of hospitalized patients. *Nursing Research*; *30(1)*: 32-37.

20. Quinn JF (1989). Therapeutic touch as energy exchanger: Replication and extension. *Nursing Science Quarterly*; *1(2)*: 79-87.

21. Jimenez AM (1994). Soothing hands for labor. *American Baby*; *54(11)*: BB10.B12.90.

22. Buenting JA (1993). Human energy fields and birth: Implications for research and practice. *Advances in Nursing Science*; *15(4)*: 53-59.

23. Meehan TC (1985). The effect of therapeutic touch on the experience of acute pain in post-operative patients. Dissertation Abstracts International, 46, 795B. (University Microfilms No. 8510765).

24. Meehan TC, Mermann CA, Wiseman ME, Wolff BB & Malgady RC (1990). Effects of therapeutic touch on post-operative pain. Presented at the Annual Meeting of Nurse Healers-Professional Associates, Toronto, Canada, November 1990.

25. Wright SM (1987). The use of therapeutic touch in the management of pain. *Nursing Clinics of North America*; *22(3)*: 705-713.

26. Mackey RB (1995). Discover the healing power of therapeutic touch. *American Journal of Nursing*; *95(4)*: 26-32.

27. Keller E & Bzdek VM (1986). Effects of therapeutic touch on tension headache pain. *Nursing Research*; *35(2)*: 101-106.

28. Wirth DP, Richardson JT, Eidelmen WS & Omalley AC (1993). Full thickness dermal wounds treated with non-contact therapeutic touch: A replication and extension. *Complementary Therapies in Medicine*; *1*: 127-132.

'h DP (1990). The effect of non-contact therapeutic touch on the healing ' full thickness dermal wounds. *Subtle Energies*; *1(1)*: 1-20.

30. Quinn JF & Strelkauskas AJ (1993). Psychoimmunologic effects of therapeutic touch on practitioners and recently bereaved recipients: A pilot study. *Advances in Nursing Science*; *15(4)*: 13-26.

31. Chiappone J (1989). *The light touch: An easy guide to hands-on-healing.* (revised edition) Lake Mary, FL: Holistic Reflections.

32. Nordoff P & Robbins C (1977). *Creative music therapy.* New York: The John Day Company.

33. Priestley M (1975). *Music therapy in action.* London: Constable.

34. Priestley M (1994). *Essays on analytical music therapy.* Phoenixville, PA: Barcelona Publishers.

35. Bruscia KE (1987). *Improvisational models of music therapy.* Springfield, IL: Charles C Thomas Publisher.

36. Krieger D & Kunz D (1995). Lectures delivered during 1995 Invitational Therapeutic Touch Workshop, Pumpkin Hollow Farm, Craryville, NY, July 21-26, 1995.

Supplemental Reading

1. Barrett EAM (Ed) (1990). *Visions of Rogers' science-based nursing.* New York: National League for Nursing.

2. Beaulieu J (1987). *Music and sound in the healing arts.* Barrytown, NY: Station Hill Press.

3. Epstein M (1995). *Thoughts without a thinker: Psychotherapy from a Buddhist perspective.* New York: Harper Collins Publishers, Inc.

4. LeShan (1974). *How to meditate.* New York: Bantam Books.

5. Nhat Hanh T (1976). *The miracle of mindfulness: A manual on meditation.* Boston, MA: Beacon Press.

Nurse Healers Professional Associates Inc, Cooperative
P.O. Box 444, Allison Park, PA 15101, USA.

The Value of Integrating Music Therapy and Expressive Arts Therapy* in Working with Cancer Patients

Anne Olofsson
Stockholm, Sweden

This paper will focus on the use of music and expressive arts in group therapy with cancer patients. Since 1990, a music therapist and an expressive arts therapist have worked in close co-operation at an oncological clinic. Based on their experience, this chapter illustrates a way of integrating the different modes of expression. This is of value in meeting the individual and matching their needs. Combining music, art, body language, poetry, etc, offers a rich spectrum of expression. Observation shows, that using these different modalities together may deepen and broaden the experience of patients.

This paper will demonstrate how music therapy and expressive arts therapy can act as a powerful complement to other treatments in an oncology setting. After a brief description of the department and a short background of therapeutic needs confronting the music therapist, the main focus will be on clinical work, describing group therapy and sharing reflections on this work.

The Oncology Department

Radiumhemmet is the oncology department of Karolinska Sjukhuset, a university hospital in Stockholm, treating about 43,000 adult cancer patients per year. In the early 1970s, a Psychosocial Unit was created, to study psychological and social problems caused by cancer, to patients, relatives and staff. The unit is staffed by psychiatrists, psychologists and specially trained nurses. I was appointed

---

*Expressive Arts Therapy is a psychotherapeutic method, where verbal and non-verbal modes of expression are combined. Verbal communication, art, music, drama, dance/ movement and poetry are used. Often the expressive arts therapist will use stories and myths, symbols, dreams and rituals to engage information from the unconscious.

to the unit in 1988. Two years later, I was joined by a nurse who is presently training to become an expressive arts therapist. We now work together, supporting each other in representing artistic and non-verbal therapies within the unit.

Our work is with of in-patients and out-patients, individually and in groups. Other activities include information and work shops. We are hoping, in the future, to engage in further training, supervision and research. We work across the boundaries of music therapy and expressive arts therapy appreciating the possibilities of these differing modalities.

Encountering Cancer

Encountering a life threatening disease can evoke existential questions as well as psychological and emotional reactions. Living with a palliative condition can touch deep into the personality. Disease implies confrontation with difficult unwanted symptoms. Most cancer patients have to face constant loss and uncertainty. It is important that subsequent experiences, feelings and thoughts are expressed and explored, in order to facilitate and support an inevitable process of grieving, towards healing and personal growth. This process may be initially hard to verbalize.

Modalities - Symbols - Creativity

Alternative modalities, such as music, art and poetry, offer complementary possibilities of expression and communication. Spoken language is exact, limiting and may be inadequate. Symbolic language, however, is more easily expresses varying nuances, feelings and ambiguity. It helps to gain deeper insight into spiritual needs and is an invitation to the world of imagery, where time, space and logical connections are of less importance. The possibilities of non-verbal expression stimulate creativity - shaping a new world of existence. The creative process supports 'the inner motion of life' and usually leads to encountering something new; a picture, symbol, feeling, idea or vision, a new reflection of self. 'The essence of expressive therapy lies in process rather than in technique, for the therapy occurs through the vehicle of psychic play rather than in the actual products of artistic production'.[1]

Samklang - 'Concord'

The weekly therapy group, 'Concord', is a Swedish version of 'Partage', a routine developed at the Royal Victoria Hospital in Montreal. Our group is open primarily to patients, relatives, staff and trainees. The group constantly changes with the continuing presence of two therapists. This provides a safe therapeutic environment.

Each patient is invited personally and we try to adapt each session to individual needs and abilities. This one hour activity takes place in a day room on the ward. Often based on a theme, a session may include relaxation, music, poetry, art, and sharing of individual experiences. Offering time for group-support, reflection and self-expression, these weekly events have become popular. They are so important that patients often put priority on scheduling this activity into their treatment programme.

Therapy Group - Rehabilitation

The Psychosocial Unit has successfully developed get-well-groups and a post-treatment rehabilitation programme. As complementary therapists, also addressing chronically ill out-patients, my colleague and I have run short-time creative therapy groups. Each group takes six to eight patients, meeting eight times on a weekly basis for two-hour sessions.

The members of groups vary in respect of diagnosis, phase of illness, age and gender. What they all have in common is their wish to be a member of this group. The objective of the group is to offer a neutral, safe and holding space for the individual, to work on his/her situation and processes. Hopefully our work will promote the patients' self-understanding and give a feeling of wholeness in spite of taxing treatment.

Case Study - Esther

Esther is a 49 year-old woman, who works in administration. She is positive, cheerful, talkative, social and loves being outdoors. She is married with a 20 year-old daughter. Esther was treated for a breast cancer about five years ago. After mastectomy and post-treatment, she was able to continue her life. Three-and-a-half years later, she developed lung and later bone metastases, undergoing chemotherapy but with limited success.

At the time she started our group, her illness had progressed and she was again undergoing chemotherapy.

Session 1

Initially, Esther asks *"Why am I here"*. She talks about her illness with little or no emotion, though seems to be moved by listening to the others. She has a playful attitude and jokes about her inability to paint.

149

Closing the first session, participants are asked to reflect on their experience, noting the first word that comes to mind. Each person says a word, accompaning it with a body movement. The group, standing in circle, reflects by doing the same. Esther expresses 'emptiness'. She lets her body fall slack with drooping head and shoulders.

Session 2

Esther states that she has had a busy week. Despite working almost full time and doing the housework, she denies any sense of fatigue. She prefers general subjects, avoiding emotional material.

Benjamin Britten's 'Saraband' from the Simple Symphony accompanies a directed imagery. Using oil pastels, Esther paints a 'Spring Promenade'. In a corner is placed a house, (only half of it is in the picture) half a door and window. The house is surrounded by a garden. There are vivid, powerful lines and dazzling colours. A path leads through the painting. There is water in the distance.

Does this picture mirror Esther? - a social, colourful person who shows little of her inner self.

Session 3

One of the group members complains about the injustice of life. Esther immediately expresses indignation and insists that her illness has enriched her life.

The main aim of the session is clay-work. Each patient is asked to create an animal whilst Pachelbel's 'Canon' is played in the background. Each animal is given a name and then presented to the group.

Esther made two animals. One is 'Sleepy', her dog, who is placed in a resting position. He's a sporting dog, very active and runs fast every day. Afterwards he is exhausted and needs a rest. He keeps a strict feeding schedule and prefers meat. He is stubborn and has a favourite corner in every room.

The other animal is 'Hans', an alligator, who lies waiting in the swamp. Esther says: *"You can hold a baby one if you tie its jaws, but I suppose only the Indians can hold the big ones. Its eyes are placed low, on the sides of its head and it has breathing holes on its head. You cannot protect yourself against it."*

Esther starts telling her story with a giggle, but suddenly a blazing blush colours her skin. She speaks slowly and emotionally. The group is moved. We feel that the group understands this portrait of herself and her illness.

Session 4

Esther talks about excercise and hours of biking and long walks during the weekend. She describes how she matches her present chemotherapy with full-time work and domestic responsibilities. When another group member airs concern about her present weakness, Esther comments: *"Oh, I'm sure it's just the weather!"*

Discussion continues, uncovering difficulties and mutual fears as well as secret hopes and dreams. Slowly Esther expresses vulnerability, admitting she was completely exhausted after the long biking tour. She still had to cook for the family, and her husband expected her to do the house. She likes to feel competent and hates falling asleep in front of the television. Blushing, her lips trembling and with tears in the eyes, she says she cannot cry. Esther then tells the group about the trauma when her baby daughter fell seriously ill and how Esther convinced herself that this was life's big struggle and that nothing worse would ever happen. *"And then I got this..."*, she says. Afterwards, group members are asked to say a few words about their present feelings. Esther says: *"Community, togetherness"*.

Coda

Esther continued to approach death through symbolic language. She said she was puzzled by a sense of deepened self-understanding, that she could feel but was unable to verbalize. The chemotherapy worked well for a while and Esther enjoyed some good months, before another relapse. In August she died.

Conclusion

In conclusion I would like to share some of Esther's evaluation.

"It is very positive to meet others in a similar life situation, to know there are others fighting low odds."

"I liked being part of a group, I felt support and encouragement. It has provided new ideas and inspiration. And made me realize that I can allow myself to feel tired and down."

About

music:	*"Relieving, relaxing, strengthening"*
painting and clay-work:	*"Felt good to be creative, I need more time for that"*
body movement:	*"Wonderful to move, it helps my brain rest"*
writing:	*"Surprising! I had no idea that I had so much knowledge, opinions, so much to express!"*
group discussion, sharing:	*"I never thought I would get so much out of that!"*
guided imagery:	*"I would have loved to do more, I discovered a new land where one can go whenever I want"*

Reference

1. Robbins A (1986). *Expressive Therapy*. New York: Human Sciences Press

Working with the Unknown: Music Therapy and Art Therapy with a Young Man with Niemann Picks Disease

Gillian Stevens and Hilary Lomas
Abergavenny, UK

In this paper we would like to describe art therapy and music therapy with a young man suffering from a very rare, inherited, neurological condition. For Niemann Picks disease to be passed on, both parents have to be carriers of the affected gene. Throughout the world only a few hundred people are known to have this disease. The cause of the condition is apparently an abnormal processing of cholesterol in the cells and the symptoms include the following:

- enlarged liver and spleen
- neurological deterioration
  - difficulties with co-ordination
  - difficulties with balance
  - decreased muscle tone
  - reduction in vertical eye movement
  - speech slurred or lost
  - difficulties in swallowing
  - mental impairment

Life-expectancy is usually shorter the earlier the neurological symptoms appear, so that a baby diagnosed with Niemann Picks disease is likely to die in childhood, whereas someone diagnosed in his mid-teens might live to be 30 or older. There is considerable variation in the known cases.

Art Therapy - Hilary Lomas
Martin's involvement with art therapy began with a referral from his key worker. Martin was clearly aware of the effects of Niemann Picks disease and as a

consequence was angry and frustrated. The referrer's aim was to give him the opportunity to deal with the build up of tensions he was experiencing. Martin was interested in art and drawing and was able to concentrate. Art therapy was felt to be a good choice of intervention. After meeting Martin and his father I arranged to see Martin each week for one hour. A trial period confirmed the therapy to be of help, and so the arrangement continued for 19 months, until I left the area to take up another post.

The next part of this paper is a brief account of the art therapy work that Martin and I did together, from the therapist's view. I look at some of the difficulties for the therapist, which are pertinent to the uncertainties and unknown nature of Niemann Picks disease.

When I met him, Martin was living with his father. His father was, and still is, his main carer. Other important people in Martin's life, apart from family members, were two support workers who took him out each morning. Martin showed no signs of Niemann Picks until his mid teens, but his condition had then deteriorated rapidly. When I met him, he was in his early twenties. He was able to walk, but was unsteady on his feet and often fell. Fortunately he had been keen on martial arts before the onset of the disease, and had retained an ability to fall well, without hurting himself. He was able to enjoy physical activities, for example swimming. He had trouble, however, in performing precise movements, such as putting tops on pens, but was able to do a fair amount for himself. Sometimes he was able to talk, usually early in the morning, to his father. He did not speak in art therapy. Most of those around him felt that he had retained his understanding of language. I also felt this to be so. There was some deterioration quite soon after our sessions started. Martin became incontinent and began to have trouble swallowing. He spoke less at home, though his understanding appeared to stay the same. After this, Martin's condition then remained fairly stable, although towards the end of the 19 months, physical activities were obviously becoming more of a strain. As a result Martin began to spend more time at home, a change which seemed to suit him.

On meeting them, it was clear that neither the father nor son wanted pity, rather they wanted to be treated with respect and given a reasonable level of help and support from the services available. Managing their situation and coping calmly and with humour was vitally important and this aspect was to underpin my sessions with Martin.

In his first session Martin established his wish to be treated with respect. His careful use of art materials indicated the importance of the issue of control over his life and body. Through tears and actions he let me know that he was also holding grief. In his second session, Martin produced a piece of art work which I will describe. The piece illustrates the dilemmas for the therapist in choosing appropriate therapeutic responses. With much effort Martin neatly wrote his name at the bottom of the paper. He then almost playfully used blue paint to cover the name completely. He repeated this process twice, with bravado, as if challenging me to make the interpretation which seemed obvious to me, that the obliterated names washed out in a sea of blue, signified his awareness of his condition, a stark portrayal of losing himself. If this was a challenge, then I did not dare to take it up. Speaking the words seemed too brutal, especially to someone who could not defend himself with words. Thinking about his picture again, one could come up with many different interpretations. Was it an illustration of the common experience of the disabled, of being treated as invisible by others? Was the picture meaningful at all? Could it have been a playful juxtaposition of paint and crayon, having no particular personal relevance? I did not know and could not decide. On one hand I felt compelled to hear him if he was attempting to speak the truth of the disease, on the other I did not want to impose my own thoughts on him if I had no permission to do so. Even in retrospect, I cannot decide if my silence concerning the content of the picture was a sound therapeutic judgement, or an avoidance of the vital issues, due to my own reluctance to face them.

Throughout art therapy there were many examples of similar situations, where, although Martin seemed to state his thoughts and feelings with great clarity, through facial expressions, and his use of the art materials, I was left full of doubts. One week, about eight months after the first example, Martin drew half a hanged man; gallows, head, arms and body. The figure was unfinished. Was this a self portrait or a child's game?

As sessions progressed, experience suggested that it was better for me to interpret, make guesses and assume meaning. Sometimes Martin would respond directly confirming or denying my suggestions, sometimes he would not. If his actions and art works were left without interpretation the atmosphere of the sessions became listless and the work seemed pointless. As time went on, Martin used the sessions with enthusiasm to work through his feelings of grief and anger surrounding his loss of control of his life and his own body, and to try to find ways that he could accept the help he needed without feeling humiliated or treated like a child.

In spite of the apparent usefulness of art therapy, communication continued to seem fraught with complications, ambiguities and contradictions. I felt like a person struggling to hold a conversation in a foreign language. It was hard to follow when the subject had been changed. To some extent I had to concentrate on the therapy itself and on the therapeutic relationship as the context for the work. I had no other framework for understanding Martin's feelings and he had no means of enlightening me.

When Gillian Stevens and I discussed our work prior to presenting this paper, we came back again and again to our doubts over our own perceptions in the sessions. The doubts persisted in spite of Martin's efforts and in spite of repeated evidence that we were, if not right all the time, at least on the right track. In art therapy I was constantly afraid of my words. Was I being too intrusive? Was I saying the right thing? In my experience these are often concerns when working with someone who is not verbal. However the feelings have a persistence when thinking about the work with Martin that makes me think they must have a specific relevance. I was reminded of Sinason[1] and wondered if my uncertainty in the sessions was actually my own defence against the horrible truth. In spite of my work with Martin, I was never fully able to believe that it was possible to live with the certainty of physical and mental deterioration. I think this truth taps into deep fears of psychic disintegration. Perhaps it was easier to think that Martin's pain was a figment of my imagination. Perhaps it would have been more comfortable to assume that Martin had little understanding. Perhaps we were both struggling to maintain a bearable balance between denial and acceptance.

In the painful journey towards acceptance, I think that Martin managed rather better than I, as in the last few months of art therapy he became calmer and appeared happier and more at ease. This period coincided with a realisation that Martin was finding physical activities more of a strain, preferring to spend more time at home. In art therapy he became less interested in the art materials. For many months prior to this he had found clay a valuable medium to vent his frustrations and anger. These changes caused me to wonder if the piece of work we had undertaken might be coming to an end. I wondered if music therapy would be of benefit, as I felt Martin would have a greater scope for expressing his feelings and engaging with another person using the variety of instruments. He would also have the opportunity of listening within the context of communication, which I felt might suit his wish to be less active. I mentioned this idea to Gillian who felt that a referral might be appropriate, and to his father who was keen for Martin to have new opportunities. When I knew I would be leaving and the art therapy would have to end, I was pleased to know that Martin would continue to have another therapy provision. The move to music therapy proved to be timely and successful.

Music Therapy - Gillian Stevens

There was a gap of two or three months after the art therapist left before Martin was able to come to music therapy on a regular basis. He began weekly sessions in a local clinic.

Before I met Martin, I spoke to his father and to Hilary. We started the sessions with some knowledge and an awareness of the unknown surrounding his condition. I knew Martin had responded to and benefited from art therapy, so hoped music therapy would also be of use. Nobody knew how long Martin might live, or how rapidly he might deteriorate. I tried to imagine how Martin might feel: to have led a normal life which then gradually disappeared.

Martin arrived for his first session in a wheelchair. There was an electric piano and various tuned and untuned percussion instruments. I explained to Martin that he could use the instruments freely; that this was a time for him to express himself in whichever way he chose. It seemed that my first task was to find a way of understanding Martin, thus enabling him to communicate. The initial sessions were mainly taken up with discovering Martin's physical and musical capabilities and preferences. I also began to interpret his wide range of facial expressions.

He seemed to indicate his choice of instrument by directing his gaze. In later sessions I realised that he was still able to walk short distances with support. He would make his choice by heading for the appropriate chair. At the piano he played quiet single notes, often with seconds or minutes between them. He often played a note adjacent to mine. Sometimes when he lifted his hand it would waver in mid-air never actually reaching the piano. I therefore experimented with ways of making the action easier for him. Fast, rhythmic music did not seem appropriate. Slow, calm music enabled him to move with more control. Physical support under his arm seemed to annoy him. Presenting a movement for him to copy or giving a verbal cue, seemed the greatest facilitator, hence we took it in turns to play quiet, single notes with enormous concentration and deliberation. He was, however, only able to sustain two or three such interchanges before lapsing into silence. I often sat silent, or played slow music when his intensity held him back. He also played quietly on percussion. He was able to

157

hold a beater between thumb and fingers and pass it from hand to hand, but had difficulty with timing co-ordination.

Over the weeks I began to think I was understanding the nuances of his facial expressions, but I was rarely sure. These expressions could be a response to music or speech. For example, he smiled as I copied a relatively loud smash on the cymbal, widened his eyes to indicate that he would like to swap instruments or scowled in annoyance at not being able to control his movements. One week, his father was incapacitated by a back problem and unable to care for Martin. When I mentioned this Martin broke into a wide smile, but I didn't know whether he was responding to the loved and familiar word, father, or displaying sophisticated black humour at the fact that his carer was now as disabled as himself.

During the first months, Martin's condition varied from week to week, but there was no overall progression or change apparent. There were times when Martin gave no eye-contact and spent great tracts of time playing with his shoelaces. There were sessions when Martin gazed directly into my eyes for long intense periods, seemingly trying to communicate. I would come away feeling unbearably sad. There were sessions when Martin focused on the instruments and used them throughout the hour. He selected instruments that responded to a minimum of physical effort; cymbal, wind-chimes and metallophone. I would place these around him within reach and support the single, quiet sounds he produced with slow, quiet music on piano or cello.

I felt I was getting to know Martin, but was constantly puzzling over the meaning of his actions. For example, was his shoelace fiddling a reassurance to himself that he could still perform basic skills or a deliberate rebuttal of myself and music-making? I was unsure if music therapy had anything to offer someone with such multiple problems and an unknown level of understanding. Martin's father told me that Martin would not attend the sessions if he did not choose to. I took this to be an indication that he was deriving some benefit from the sessions.

During the summer there was a three week break. The next session took place in a different location. Martin was alert and responsive. We played the piano and he sustained our turn-taking interaction for longer than usual. When I asked him questions about his break he responded with clear nods. After a while he indicated that he would like to move to the metallophone and took my hands for support. Instead of sitting down when we reached the chair he remained standing, holding my hands loosely. I talked about the summer break, then after several minutes, (wondering if he had lost track of his original intention) I asked him whether he wanted to sit down, adding that I realised he did not really require my support to do so. Instead of sitting he grasped my hands firmly and looked at me intently. I commented that maybe he was telling me that he did need my support and had missed it during the summer. I remembered that in the previous session, as I was singing Good-bye, he had fallen sideways off his chair, not a normal occurrence in our sessions. We continued to stand for a long time, maybe ten minutes, during which Martin loosened one hand and, still gazing at me, turned his empty trouser pocket inside-out. Then he was ready to sit and continue playing.

Since the Autumn a new phase has begun. He seems angrier, often refusing assistance, playing louder. He has also started to play groups of notes; scale fragments on piano and fast, quiet, repeated notes on cymbal or metallophone. I am surprised, not having expected this development in his abilities. The long silences and ambiguities also continue: is he knocking my hand from the piano or reaching across to play the note next to mine? Perhaps it does not matter whether I know the answers to these questions. What is important is that I can enter Martin's slow, quiet world. I can be with him without having to understand the meaning of every gesture, without pressure on him. I can be with him in the uncertainty that is part of all our lives.

Reference
1. Sinason, Valerie (1991). Interpretations that feel horrible to make and a theoretical unicorn. *Journal of child psychotherapy* Vol.17.

Part Six

Neurological Conditions

On the Vegetative State:
Music and Coma Arousal Interventions

Mary Elinor Boyle
New York, USA

Medical literature reports many coma arousal interventions involving intensive sensory stimulation programs for patients in vegetative states following acute coma. Experimental replication of these procedures has produced antithetical results. The issues in this controversy relate to outcome measures, primarily awareness versus arousal. They are closely tied to difficulties implicit in the diagnosis itself. Levy, Knill-Jones and Plum[1] in discussing the diagnosis explain, 'The common denominator is the appearance of wakefulness without any external evidence of communication or complex behaviour.'

Care givers are confronted with patients for whom it is very difficult to know what type of care may be appropriate. Controversy concerning the appropriateness and/or effectiveness of sensory stimulation procedures has extended to encompass questioning the viability of the diagnosis, 'the vegetative state'. Certain authors suggest a change in the terminology to: 'minimally responsive patients',[2] 'prolonged coma', or 'post-comatose unawareness'[3] and 'post-comatose unresponsiveness'.[4] Since the diagnosis of the vegetative state was first described by Jennett and Plum in 1972,[5] researchers have been testing assessments of awareness for these patients. The complexity of the problem is evident in post-mortem studies.

> The distribution and severity of post-mortem anatomical damage to the cerebral hemispheres can vary considerably in vegetative patients, making it difficult to infer on pathological grounds alone whether or not all self-awareness was lost during life. Such uncertainty can be resolved only by additional objective measures of brain function in these patients.[6]

Plum and Posner[7] hold that 'Behaviourally, one can estimate another person's self-aware consciousness only by his response to the examiner's verbal commands or gestures.'

The music therapist is in a unique position to elicit responses to verbal directions. We work with a client's strength rather than his/her deficit. Often coma arousal interventions incorporate music via cassette tapes or radio programming. Sometimes, this merely involves turning on a radio. Whether these passive listening procedures constitute treatment is an issue with patients in vegetative states because outcome is an issue. Will there be one (which is recognisable to others)? What outcome do we expect from the procedure(s)?

Some may question whether outcome should be an issue. An assumption is made that audio stimulation could not be aversive. Any music therapist who ponders this assumption will question it. The diversity in musical preference of our patients is at moments overwhelming.

In this chapter I will review research findings on several coma arousal interventions and discuss how music therapists can employ an operant technique to assess and develop systematic responses to verbal directions or questions. This can be seen as an awareness outcome. Operant behaviours are those shaped by their consequences. Operant procedures are those procedures which attempt to develop operant behaviours using positive reinforcement. Preferred music which follows a correct response is an example of an operant procedure. There is extensive literature on music in operant procedures.[8] Dorow[9] demonstrated an operant music procedure to be effective with profoundly retarded non-verbal clients. This appears ideal for patients with this diagnosis - one relating to lack of responsiveness to external stimuli. If we can develop operant behaviours (in this case systematic motor responses), then we may be able to train these behaviours as communicative responses to questions. The typical format would be a 'yes/no/maybe' single-word response system correlated to simple motor behaviours.

Sensory Stimulation Protocols

It is common practice in custodial care settings to have televisions and radios playing in patients rooms. Wood[10] questions whether there is a rationale for 'sensory stimulation'. He cautions that:

> *"arousal and awareness are different conditions of cerebral activity. The target of sensory stimulation should be to try to access what might remain of the latter, rather than just increase the level of the former because only awareness is related to measurable changes of behaviour;*

and accepted international measures, such as the Glasgow Coma Scale, evaluate changes in awareness rather than arousal."

Wood suggests that rather than sensory stimulation, sensory regulation should take place.

In contrast, Mitchell et al[11] trained family members to perform 'programmes of vigorous sensory stimulation'. Each of the five senses was stimulated five times in a cycle. There could be several cycles in a day (up to eight hours a day, seven days a week). With a population of 24 patients in either treatment or control group, Mitchell et al[11] reported that the total duration of coma was shorter for the coma arousal procedure group than the control.

Pierce et al[12] found no significant difference using the coma arousal procedure with a population of 31. The technique for assessment of outcome they used was the time taken to obey a simple command on two consecutive occasions 24 hours apart, and the score on the Glasgow Outcome Scale 10-12 mos post-injury. Wilson et al[13] reported on a ten minute multimodal stimulation procedure with four patients which resulted in increases in the time the patients' eyes were open. They assumed that this indicated increased arousal.

I began examining issues in sensory stimulation as a result of an operant treatment procedure used in previous research.[14] My questions involved whether other operant sensory stimuli would be as effective as music. Was it possible to develop an assessment technique to determine which vegetative patients would benefit from an operant music procedure? Would some patients benefit more from another sensory medium, i.e. videotapes, fans or lights?

I developed an assessment protocol[15] involving four to sixteen 30-minute sessions consisting of two 10-minute sensory stimulation segments and one 10-minute baseline segment. The number of sessions varied because I expected certain patients to respond immediately while others would require more sessions to develop systematic motor response patterns. A simple switch which required an 'active' (patient initiated) rather than a 'passive' (therapist initiated) response was used to analyse patient non-verbal responses to external sensory stimuli in contrast to baseline. This is an important procedural difference from the typical sensory stimulation protocol in which the therapist or family member manipulates sensory stimuli and waits for a patient response. By presenting the patient with a motor task involving turning on and off certain electrical stimuli, I hoped to demonstrate learning via graphs of learning curves. A major postulate related to awareness as an outcome. I 'hoped' that awareness would be an outcome generalisation if it was possible to develop systematic responses to stimuli.

Response Definitions and Data Collection Procedures

Two responses, pillow pressing and pillow releasing, activated one of four sensory conditions or baseline. Pillow pressing consisted of pressing lightly on a pressure sensitive pillow switch. Pillow releasing consisted of following a pillow press with a decrease in pressure on the pillow switch. The changes in pressure activated electronic appliances, i.e. a cassette recorder, a videotape machine, a fan, a light, or under baseline condition, nothing. The changes in pressure were recorded on an Esterline Angus Event Recorder.

Sensory Stimuli

The choice of music or videotapes was determined by conversations with the family. If the family told me of a specific preference, then that tape was presented. If the family knew of no preferences, then I presented a comedy video of a program which the patient could never have seen before onset of coma. In the case of music, I employed tapes of popular songs from the patient's adolescent and early adult years.

The stimuli were activated by a timer apparatus which turned the appliances on and off in 15 or 20 second intervals. The experimenter set the timer in terms of the patient's ability to move to reactivate the pillow.

Procedural Efficacy

Several patients[15] demonstrated differential responses to the stimuli. In most cases the comedy video and 'Oldies but Goodies' cassette tapes elicited similar response rates, while the light and fan were least preferred or avoided. Learning curves were evident with certain patients and not clearly evident with others. With patients who did not demonstrate learning curves over several days, there were 'on good days' differential response rates to stimuli.

Anecdotal recording procedures assumed more importance than was originally anticipated. The significance or power of a response to external stimuli was often most evident under this recording procedure for those patients not demonstrating clear learning curves. One patient waved the pillow at me while throwing up her hands during baseline following a video segment. She clearly knew, at that moment, the switch was not working for 'The Cosby Show'. Another patient cried whenever the video or cassette recorder went off after a 15-second interval.

Future Directions

The issue in assessment and treatment procedures with vegetative patients is awareness as an outcome. The reason family members are willing to co-operate in sensory stimulation protocols involving many hours of their time is that they expect to get responses to their interactions. As one mother told me, *"All I want is for my daughter to look at me when I say her name"*.

Variability in responsiveness is the overriding characteristic of this diagnosis, as can be seen in the diagnostic controversy. When family members see the positive side of the variability, then they want further services for the patient. The Glasgow Coma Scale[16,17] analyses the patient's best responses to stimuli over given time periods. Music therapists should examine a patient's best responses and then develop a protocol to enhance them. A baseline procedure, however, is always necessary to examine treatment effectiveness. Concurrent schedule, or multi-element baseline designs[18,19] are useful because they incorporate treatment and baseline procedures concurrently.

Due to response variability, several strategies need to be employed to document responsiveness to external stimuli. Frequency and/or duration recording needs to be employed to demonstrate systematic responses. With this type of recording, the therapist can develop a sense of the range of possibilities for the patient in terms of systematic responses. The therapist can graph responses to examine linear trends in the data. One can also calculate means and analyse the numerical range of responses. This type of data is essential due to the minimal responsiveness characteristic of the diagnosis. There are often so few responses in the initial stages of a procedure that a caregiver would not recognise improvement without the aid of data-based techniques. However, within a few weeks some change should be evident.

Anecdotal recording may give us the largest window for observing the patient's strength. For example, when family or staff members saw a patient laughing appropriately they were often dismayed. One patient's husband began sobbing. It was very difficult for me to watch a patient struggle to touch the switch and then to put her nose on the television monitor within the 20-second interval of the Mets game. When the patient's physician observed this two days in a row, he ordered new testing and patient treatment programming immediately. Anecdotal recording can also document changes in the topography of a patient's response to stimuli. As the patient develops strength, the therapist may note a change from finger movements appearing initially as tics to hand grabbing/holding.

The procedures one uses are critical to documentation of responses. The procedures involving music must be simple and systematic. If a mechanised procedure is not possible, a discrete trial protocol using a simple motor behaviour would be preferred. The client needs to be presented with a task that can be performed. The therapist should choose a spontaneous motion which has been witnessed during an observation period. Initial trials should be physically guided. The therapist should assess whether verbal prompts are appropriate. (For certain aphasic patients, verbal prompts may be contra-indicated. Determining whether a profoundly head-injured patient is aphasic is complicated.)

Work with profoundly head-injured clients means that ethical, 'quality of life', and human behavioural issues come to the fore. I remember working with one of my patients who was diagnosed as neocortically brain-dead by two neurologists and one neurosurgeon. As I was waiting for a response in 10-second intervals, I remember questioning what life was for my patient. One of the difficult aspects of working with her involved observing her eye movements which were asynchronous. I wondered if I should be disturbing a person in this state. Yet, as I watched her spasm and expunge breath, I realized I was not convinced that she did not feel pain. This was especially challenging to me after she developed systematic responses under operant treatment conditions.[14] As a result of using 15-second intervals of Linda Ronstadt recordings as reinforcement for correct responses to the researcher's directions, the patient developed eye focus with family and staff members who said her name. Family and staff members said it was much easier to care for her when she focussed her eyes on them. (Staff members understood that the patient was neocortically blind.) This patient taught me how important it is to attempt to understand a patient at his or her performance level. If we do not know any level of performance, then we need to develop a protocol appropriate to the patient. We must remember that music is primal. At least one neocortically brain-dead patient has made systematic responses to music. The meaning of those acts is not a comfort to me, however. McQuillen[20] comments upon the challenge presented to our society implicit in the maintenance of persons of whom we have no knowledge of whether appropriate treatment procedures could alleviate their pain or provide pleasure.

The American Academy of Neurology holds, ...'that there is no behavioural indication of pain perception and that unconscious patients do not experience pain.'[21] Spudis[21] explains that 'by definition, pain cannot be perceived by mindless patients'. However, in a June 1990 survey by the ANA, 44 per cent of several hundred members said they were uncertain whether PVS patients perceived pain and 27 per cent were equally uncertain if the word 'suffering' could be substituted for 'pain'. Doherty[22] reported that a patient in a vegetative state is capable of a normal hormonal response to pain. (The 'vegetative state' is differentiated from the 'persistent vegetative state').

It appears that the question for music therapists is one of humanity. Why stimulate a person in a vegetative state? Because we are attempting to care for a human being, who is in an altered state of being. Families and professionals observe behavioural indicators of pain. We see a patient contract, expunge breath, moan; we observe pupils dilate. We pray that they do not 'perceive' pain, although they may have normal hormonal responses to pain. Given my research in 1983 with a neocortically brain-dead patient who made systematic operant responses to 15-second intervals of Linda Ronstadt, I would question our concept of the word 'perceive'. It appears that despite our conceptions of humanity in terms of abstraction, cognition, awareness, etc, as long as we are alive we are human beings in varied states of being. To understand humanity we should address issues such as the relationship of awareness to arousal and the philosophical and medical meanings of the terms awareness, thought and cognition. What are measures of humanness - laughter, tears? Is thought only cortical? As music therapists, we should address these issues in terms of patient responses to music. Does the patient smile or cry only during a particular phrase? Does the patient tap a beat to a jig while 'listening'? How can I train a motor behaviour which has multiple uses?

Effective treatment is at issue here, due to fiscal as well as humanitarian realities. If the music therapist cannot demonstrate potential benefit on an individual client basis, then it would appear better that we serve others who can receive benefit from our services. The challenge to the therapist to determine how to demonstrate benefit for a client with profound and diffuse brain injury may appear overwhelming. However, we begin with a movement which is within the patient's repertoire so that staff can observe a patient initiated response. In order for the patient to know what it is that we are expecting as a response, it may be necessary physically to guide the desired response. For example, the therapist might ask a patient to squeeze his or her eyes shut twice. If the patient does not respond within 10 seconds to the therapist's request, the therapist would gently close the patient's eyelids slowly twice. A similar procedure could be followed for head nods or head turns depending upon the patient's movement patterns.

To date, there has been no demonstration of treatment benefit for patients who receive extensive and in many cases exhaustive passive stimulation. In the future, someone may demonstrate clinical efficacy with a passive stimulation procedure.

However, as there has been no demonstration of benefit for these procedures, there are critical ethical questions that music therapists must address. Should I manipulate this human being in this way when she/he cannot control the duration of the procedure? This is an important consideration especially due to the effects on perception that severe brain damage can have. It may be that what we would consider 'listening' could be a 'sonic assault' on the client.

We must attempt to evoke 'awareness' responses rather than mere 'arousal' responses. Allowing patients to activate and deactivate sound or video sources may give them as much control as they may know over their environment and lives. Training responses relative to and interactive with these actions may allow a patient to become receptive again to the environment in which he or she lives. The elicitation or evocation of awareness responses also demands that the therapist become an advocate for effective treatment programming for the client. The obvious step after developing a systematic response is to help the client use that response in a communicative way. This may involve training family members to ask questions that can be answered using a yes/no/maybe signal. Some may question why a music therapist would train communicative responses. I suggest that we should train communicative skills because we have been successful in training simple responses to music. The client is 'aware' that we acknowledge his/her strengths.

Despite the political position of the ANA concerning pain perception, LaPuma et al[23] gave this advice to physicians, which is encouragement for us as well: *"Talk to comatose patients, 'because they may hear, because some comatose patients may get better, and because we are caring professionals'."*

References

1. Levy DE, Knill-Jones RP & Plum F (1978). The vegetative state and its prognosis following non-traumatic coma. *Annals of the New York Academy of Sciences*, *315*: 293-306.

2. Giacino JT, Kezmarsky MA, De Luca J & Cicerone KD (1991). Monitoring rate of recovery to predict outcome in minimally responsive patients. *Archives of Physical Medicine and Rehabilitation*, *72*: 897-901.

3. Sazbon L & Groswasser Z (1991). Prolonged coma, vegetative state, post-comatose unawareness: semantics or better understanding? *Brain Injury*, *5(1)*: 1-2.

4.   Glenn MB (1992). Post-comatose unawareness? *Brain Injury*, *6*: 101-102.

5.   Jennett B & Plum F (1972). Persistent vegetative state after brain damage: a syndrome in search of a name. *Lancet*, *94*: 734-737.

6.   Levy DE, Sidtis JJ, Rottenberg DA, Jarden JO, Strother SC, Dhawan V, Ginos JZ, Tramo MJ, Evans AC & Plum F (1987). *Annals of Neurology*, *22(6)*: 673-682.

7.   Plum F & Posner JB (1980). *The diagnosis of stupor and coma*. Philadelphia: FA Davis Company.

8.   Greer RD (1981). An operant approach to motivation and affect: ten years of research in music learning. In: *Documentary Report of the National Symposium on the Applications of Psychology to the Teaching and Learning of Music*. Washington DC: MENC Press.

9.   Dorrow LG (1975). Conditioning music and approval as new reinforcers for imitative behaviour with the severely retarded. *Journal of Music Therapy*, *12*: 33-39.

10. Wood RL (1991). Critical analysis of the concept of sensory stimulation for patients in vegetative states. *Brain Injury*, *5(4)*: 401-409.

11. Mitchell S, Bradley VA, Welch JL & Britton PG (1990). Coma arousal procedure: a therapeutic intervention in the treatment of head injury. *Brain Injury*, *4(3)*: 273-279.

12. Pierce JP, Lyle DM, Quine S, Evans NJ & Morris J (1990). The effectiveness of coma arousal intervention. *Brain Injury*, *4(2)*: 191-197.

13. Wilson SL, Powell GE, Elliott K & Thwaites H (1991). Sensory stimulation in prolonged coma: four single case studies. *Brain Injury*, *5(4)*: 393-400.

14. Boyle ME & Greer RD (1983). Operant procedures and the comatose patient. *Journal of Applied Behavior Analysis*, *16*: 3-12.

15. Boyle ME (in press). An operant assessment procedure for patients in the vegetative state. In: Sato M, Sugiyama N & Boyle M (eds). *Theoretical and applied issues in behaviour analysis*. Osaka, Japan: Niheisha Publications.

16. Habbema JDF, Braakman R & Avezaat CJJ (1979). Prognosis of the individual patient with severe head injury. *Acta Neurochirurgia, Suppl 28*: 158-160.

17. Teasdale G, Murray G, Parker L & Jennett B (1979). Adding up the Glasgow coma score. *Acta Neurochirurgia*; *28*: 13-16.

18. Hersen M & Barlow DH (1975). *Single case experimental designs*. New York: Pergamon Press.

19. Ulman JD & Sulzer-Azaroff B (1975). Multi-element baseline design in educational research. In: Ramp E & Semb G (eds). *Behavior analysis: Areas of research and application*. Englewood Cliffe NJ: Prentice-Hall.

20. McQuillen MP (1991). Can people who are unconscious or in the "vegetative state" perceive pain? *Issues in Law and Medicine, 6(4)*: 373-383.

21. Spudis EV (1991). The persistent vegetative state - 1990. *Journal of the Neurological Sciences, 102*: 128-136.

22. Doherty DL (1988). Can vegetative patients feel pain? *Archives of Physical Medicine and Rehabilitation, 69*: 721.

23. La Puma J, Schiedermayer DL, Gulyas AE & Siegler (1988). Talking to comatose patients. *Archives of Neurology, 45*: 20-22.

Music Therapy as Part of Assessment and Treatment for People Living with Huntington's Disease

Wendy Magee
London, UK

Introduction

The ideas presented in this paper are a reflection of a four-year period working with people living with Huntington's Disease (HD). I will draw together issues about my development as therapist, alongside the client's path of progressive deterioration, exploring what approaches best meet the client's abilities and how the therapist can best support these needs. A definition and description of the symptoms of HD are given, followed by behaviours and responses observed through various case studies.

Definition and description of Huntington's Disease

Huntington's disease is a chronic, progressive, hereditary condition that affects the central nervous system. It stems from basal ganglia damage within the brain. It causes motor, cognitive and emotional disorders, and although the average age of onset is 36-45 years of age, symptoms may emerge at any time from childhood to old age.[1] It is an autosomal dominant disorder (each child born to a parent with the HD gene has a 50 per cent chance of also carrying the gene and developing the disease). It is not HD which causes death, but secondary illness such as pneumonia or cardiorespiratory illness. These have been found to be the most common causes of death.[2,1]

The illness is characterised by involuntary 'choreic' movements and abnormality of voluntary movements, gradual deterioration of certain cognitive skills and emotional disorders causing complex social consequences for the individual and their family or support network. Problems may involve large, sweeping movements or rigidity and slowness involving arms, legs, fingers, trunk, neck, head and face. Speech becomes dysrhythmic, slower, or dysarthric, causing the listener difficulty in interpreting the spoken message. Difficulty in initiating speech may cause considerable delay in responding to simple requests or commands. Swallowing problems develop, and in the later stages the use of direct feeding methods such as nasogastric tube or gastrostomy may be necessary to ensure adequate nutrition.

Early cognitive symptoms are likely to involve memory problems and an inability to organise information. These result in decreased problem-solving, initiation and concentration. Cognitive deficits may also cause difficulty with the following abilities: verbal expression; the ability to change from one task to another; retrieval of information and memories; and the speed with which information can be processed and acted upon. There is a marked loss of spontaneity and a reduced ability to participate in novel situations. Consciousness related functions such as knowing and insight, however, may be relatively well preserved even into the most advanced stages of the illness.[3]

Psychiatric disorders associated with HD may be evident years before the illness is diagnosed, resulting in distress and often stigma for the affected individual and their family. Depression, irritability and apathy are the most often exhibited symptoms, with other psychiatric conditions commonly being seen such as schizophrenia, delusional disorders, mania and anxiety. Behavioural problems and personality changes may include sexual inappropriateness, aggressive behaviour, suicidal tendencies and drug and alcohol abuse. The psychosocial effects on all concerned can be devastating.

Literature review

A review of the literature shows that music therapy is beneficial as part of music and movement programmes,[4,5] (a) as relaxation,[4] (b) to facilitate speech through singing,[6,7,4] (c) to act as a catalyst for discussion and emotion through song writing and (d) through song choice.[8,9,10] The last technique which was also described as 'counselling-oriented music therapy', appears to be relevant when working with people in the early or advanced stages of HD. This justifies it as an attractive and useful tool as other interventions become unrealistic or impossible to participate in.

Judging from the literature, it would seem that the use of familiar songs offers an easily measurable activity for research or evaluation purposes in therapy programmes, particularly important in the current climate of proving 'effectiveness' to employers. The use of improvisation is only briefly described[7] and leaves a question as to what the benefits are of this activity, considering the certainty of physical disability and cognitive degeneration. This paper attempts to explore and contrast the use of both familiar and improvised music.

What does music therapy have to offer?
Music therapy can offer a range of experiences which may be denied the person living with HD.

Even when large choreic, or minimal movements make functional tasks difficult, playing instruments can provide a purpose for attempting exploration of the environment. For clients with uncontrolled voluntary movements, using instruments with large surface areas (bass xylophones, large headed drums and cymbals) optimises success in achieving sound for the often enormous effort involved. For those with minimal rigid movements, instruments suspended on a stand (triangle or wind chimes), positioned close to the hand, allow independence in achieving feedback for this effort. Other instruments can provide maintenance and development of fine motor skills, such as keyboard, or strumming instruments which involve fine-finger movements or the manipulation of a plectrum. Encouraging decision-making through instrument choice is an added creative and expressive component to exploration, particularly when there may be few areas where the client is able or allowed to express choice or make decisions.

As speech becomes increasingly difficult, and the content seemingly meaningless or perseverative, it is likely that attempting verbal communication may be a highly frustrating experience. Music-making, through singing or playing, can alleviate this, to some extent, by providing opportunities for creative expression non-verbally.

Problems of isolation occur when there is difficulty in communication, changes in behaviour and physical deterioration. Employment may cease, and the person may become increasingly self-conscious. Opportunities for socialising decrease and relationships with family and friends are affected. The opportunity to build relationships may be impaired, though in music therapy relationships may be creatively developed. This can be the case particularly for people who have had an active background in music-making or appreciation. Lastly, music-making can act as a powerful motivator even when the person's ability to initiate is impaired.

Music therapy in the early stages
In the early stages, the person is likely to maintain a semblance of an independent lifestyle, living at home and possibly still employed. Physical symptoms may not

cause serious disability; however they will be noticeable in walking patterns, facial expression, etc. Cognitive changes may cause problems with short-term memory and tasks which involve the ability to organise, calculate, or carry out complex processes. The individual may experience behavioural or psychiatric changes, causing bizarre, unreasonable or aggressive behaviour. This may seriously affect the spouse or children living with them, and can result in marital breakdown. Emotional liability, confusion and social withdrawal are the most commonly reported responses to the often dramatic changes that occur.[11]

The picture of the person living with the early stages is one of increasing isolation and emotional turmoil. Changes in behaviour may mean outbursts of aggression, or delusional beliefs that cause immense stress to the person's support network. If insight is impaired, the client may experience confusion as to why situations around them do not make sense, or why others are behaving in such an inexplicable way. Previous occupations or pastimes gradually become impossible due to physical change; communicating with speech becomes increasingly frustrating; and the possibility of experiencing something novel or pleasurable appears greatly diminished.

In the author's experience, clients at this stage may benefit from individual sessions: giving space to take risks and to reflect on their feelings and experiences. Group work can be difficult if a client is placed with other HD clients at different stages. The client here may have to confront painful issues about their own potential deterioration.

The aim of music therapy is to engage in musical activity by focusing on the creative and expressive qualities of music. The client is encouraged to explore the dynamics of music as widely as possible. Their right of choice is always respected. During all musical experiences the client is encouraged to be actively involved. The music therapist attempts to assess the client's ability to organise information, remember previous material, interact musically, and monitor repetition of very familiar material. The therapist aims to draw on the client's strengths and work toward maintaining and developing them. Areas which need particular consideration include the client's ability to initiate change, which can affect their ability to stop playing at the end of a musical activity or change from one activity to another. Incessant repetition, or perseveration in the music may continue from one task to the next. Memory deficits combined with an inability to stop playing may cause turn-taking activities to be inappropriate, as even simple instructions are not retained or followed. Using familiar songs, the music therapy session may provide a safe environment in which to vocalise, which may be becoming increasingly difficult in other situations.

Case Study: Joseph

Joseph, a man in his mid forties, having recently been diagnosed with HD, was referred to music therapy on his admission to a day care centre. He was reported to be experiencing changing behaviour and increasing isolation, due to his perceived 'uncertain future'. Still ambulant, he walked with large swaying movements. Ataxia in both arms caused his intentional movement to be clumsy and jerky. His speech was slurred, the content often repetitive and limited in variation. He was reported to have moderately impaired memory and had started to exhibit some delusional beliefs. When he was referred to music therapy, the team hoped that it might provide an 'emotional outlet and means of expression', as his verbal communication appeared limited. He had no previous musical experience.

In nine months of attending music therapy sessions, Joseph stated that he enjoyed sessions, and appeared to gain confidence in his new found skill. Activities centred around instrumental playing, mainly through improvisation with the therapist.

Joseph expressed preference for the metallophone and electric piano - 'pipe organ' mode - though he appeared to have difficulty in exploring more than one instrument per session. Joseph tended to stay on the first chosen instrument unless I prompted change. Unless activities had a definite beginning and end, such as a song-based activity, he had difficulty stopping playing at the end of a phrase. Joseph appeared to rely on visual prompts, such as the therapist changing body posture, to conclude an activity. He was able to repeat only the simplest rhythms, and when given more complex patterns, would return the correct number of sounds but with no rhythmic organisation. This was due to a combination of difficulty with organising information and problems of co-ordination; if the given pulse was slow he was more able to repeat it with accuracy. Joseph had difficulty in turn-taking, though this reduced if the therapist was sharing the same instrument. Generally, he became engrossed in his own playing, he appeared to have little awareness of the therapist's music, regardless of dramatic dynamic, rhythmic or harmonic variations. Joseph's playing involved repeated descending and ascending scales, or repeated playing of small areas of the instrument. A typical repetitive pattern was three descending notes on the piano or metallophone, or three or four strings on the autoharp or guitar, despite being physically able to reach the full range. Overall, his playing showed a lack of spontaneity, with repeated patterns on which he seemed 'stuck', and a tendency to organise his playing spatially.

The changes during music therapy included Joseph becoming more aware of musical endings, particularly the familiar 'welcome chant'. Joseph also extended his playing of the keyboard to two hands, though he remained unable to co-ordinate his movements on the metallophone. His exploration on the keyboard expanded from simple scales to more complex patterns, combining sustained notes and slow trills or leaping intervals of fourths or thirds. These, however, soon become continually repetitive. His playing continued to lack spontaneity. It was therefore thought that using verbal suggestions might heighten his awareness of what was happening and help cause a shift in his perseveration.

Music therapy in the middle stages

People in the middle stages of HD may still be ambulant, although they experience increasing difficulty in maintaining their balance. It is more likely, at this stage, that a wheelchair becomes necessary. Choreic movements become more obvious, and the individual is more dependent on overall care. Communication is severely impaired, as speech is poorly articulated, inappropriate in content, or may occur in 'bursts'. If cognitive skills allow, the person may be able to use a communication aid, dependent on their wish to use it. Poor initiation can affect speech and behaviour, requiring an immense amount of time for a delayed response to even the simplest request. Cognitive deficits may come into play here as the person may have increasing difficulty organising and processing information, concentrating on tasks presented, or remembering instructions given. Behaviour may be generally unpredictable, and requests can result in an absence of response, refusal to comply, or in angry or aggressive outbursts.

From the author's experience, group music therapy can be beneficial at this time because it allows a natural 'time out' from activities which require attention or concentration. Group sessions can allow the client the time needed for delayed responses, using others' turns as a prompt or visual model of activity. Choice-making may be the focus of tasks, particularly with instruments that can be chosen non-verbally. Music, instrumental or vocal, should be highly structured to facilitate organisation of information, using either familiar songs, improvisations based on familiar melodies, or activities where there is a gap within the music framework for creating sounds. The structure provided by familiar songs can also aid clients with memory deficits, and can facilitate spontaneous participation for those with initiation difficulties. Songs are also useful for those who no longer have functional speech, encouraging verbalisation of rehearsed lines. Alternately, activities may remain non-verbal in the form of instrument playing.

Case study: Caroline

Caroline, a 50-year-old woman, was hospitalised when it became apparent that she was unable to care for herself on a daily basis. She had several children who were thought to be showing early behavioural symptoms of HD. On admission she was withdrawn and would refuse to participate in any form of activity by becoming verbally aggressive. Her contact with music therapy began with occasional attendance of a group with other HD clients who were in more advanced stages than herself.

Caroline later started to attend another music therapy group with people who had other conditions and hence different types of abilities and difficulties. Her speech, due to dysarthria, was almost incomprehensible, and she had impaired awareness of others. This resulted in poor social skills. She initially received mixed reactions from other members in the group who were all articulate. They had trouble understanding why she did not respond verbally to their greetings and interactions. She was highly responsive to instruments, and expressed pleasure through facial gestures during instrumental activities. These experiences helped others in the group become more accepting of her. Although her memory and cognition could not be assessed by conventional neuropsychological tests, her behaviour in music therapy suggested that she was carrying material over from one week to the next. This was shown by her recall of the welcome song and her precision in choosing a different instrument each week.

As Caroline's speech was severely impaired, she rarely spoke. She often sang, however, particularly the welcome and other familiar songs. The emphasis in the group was on non-verbal activities, particularly choosing instruments. This was something over which she took a great deal of time and thought. Instrument playing appeared to give her enormous pleasure. She became animated, in stark contrast to her behaviour in other settings when she tended to be still, interacting very little with her surrounding environment.

179

Problems which needed to be worked around included her delayed physical and verbal responses to questions or requests. This meant that the rest of the group had to wait for the time she needed to choose an instrument or song. Turn-taking activities were not appropriate due to the complexity of instructions and difficulty in stopping playing and 'passing a turn'. Often actions or instructions needed to be broken down into steps to facilitate processing of information and serve as a prompt. The use of familiar music in structured activities appeared to enable her to participate to her maximum level of functioning and respond more spontaneously.

Through her enthusiasm and interest in playing, Caroline gradually became more popular within the group. The other members appeared to become more accepting of her non-verbal participation. Whilst music was kept familiar and tasks involved instrument playing, she was able to participate to her maximum.

Music therapy in the advanced stages

The client is likely to become completely dependent, and have severely reduced opportunities for participation. Due to the high level of care needed, the family may choose to place their relative into care. By this stage, conventional feeding methods may have been replaced by alternatives such as gastrostomy or nasogastric feeding. Communication may be only through indication of 'yes/no' or, in some cases, completely absent. Choreic movements may render all functional or voluntary activity impossible. This may be disturbing to observe for family or those unfamiliar with the disease. Movements are normally constant, only ceasing during sleep, and the individual may require an enormous calorie intake - 5000 each day - to obtain adequate nutrition for the amount of energy being used.

It is important at this stage, that the therapist structures all activities around the client's remaining skills. Clients may still be able to intentionally turn their head or gaze toward a specific target, to communicate 'yes/no' by pointing to communication cards, or to play instruments which give maximum feedback for minimal rigid movements. It is unlikely that intentional vocalisation will remain.

Group music therapy is recommended. This focuses on the client and their turn within the activity, thus giving other members a break. Music found to be the most beneficial in keeping clients' attention are familiar songs, or improvisations structured on familiar tunes. Songs which include the participants' names, as part of welcome or good-bye activities, are particularly useful in helping to maintain the client's attention, and keep them oriented within the group. If a client can still turn his/her head, this may be incorporated into a welcome activity; they can turn to one another to pass on the 'hello'. Music which has been a particular favourite in the past can be discovered by talking to family members, and can be introduced to the group as having a special meaning for the client involved. Live music appears to maintain attention better than recorded music.

Finally, the family may be involved at this stage. There may be few occasions where a family member may observe their relative being purposefully involved in an activity, and few opportunities for them to share something meaningful. Music therapy can offer a chance to express humour or sadness within a contained, supportive environment. Although the techniques outlined here highlight the severe disability of the population, the opportunity to actively engage in music-making or decision making should not be dismissed lightly. This may be the only chance when such an opportunity is available.

Case study: Ted

Ted, a man in his fifties, was dependent for all aspects of daily living. He had only minimal rigid movements. Ted remained sufficiently cognitively intact to use a simple communication board and was able to respond to simple questions, and particularly humour which had always been a strong part of his personality. His communication board was limited, having only 'yes', 'no' and several other functional words written on it, to which he pointed with his finger. When Ted needed to communicate, he was dependent on someone presenting the communication board. If he could not make his wishes clear he would sometimes become frustrated. Ted stayed mostly in his room watching the television, apart from visits from his brother and nursing staff. Ted had previously been an active sportsman. He also enjoyed playing in a band. Ted was isolated, with limited opportunity for interacting with others.

Ted attended a music therapy group for four to six people in the advanced stage of HD. His participation consisted of choice making and actively playing instruments. Ted chose instruments by either looking towards one of a choice of two, or communicating 'yes/no' through his communication board. Ted's favoured instruments included the maracas (in both hands), and triangle placed on a stand, which he played with a lightweight beater. During a 'good-bye improvisation' which was played each week, Ted made great effort to achieve sounds from his instrument.

He played only when his name was sung, indicating full awareness of the musical structure. Songs which had been past favourites or that he had played in his band were discovered through discussion with his brother, and were incorporated into activities. This encouraged Ted's brother to be involved in something they could actively share. The group also provided opportunities for reminiscence and communication between the brothers.

Summary

The person with HD presents very complex symptoms and problems. The ideas presented in this paper have been formulated after considerable observation of a group of clients, in an attempt to make sense of the responses observed. The author suggests that the brain.damage caused by the disease also has an effect on the music made by clients with HD. In the author's experience, working with people affected by HD can bring up overwhelming feelings of confusion and loss. It is hoped that this discussion might help music therapists who are unfamiliar with HD better understand their client's responses, and in turn provide opportunities for maximum creativity.

Music therapy has a vital role to play in a treatment programme for a person living with HD. However, the music therapist needs to be aware not only of the emotional and physical effects of the illness, but also the client's cognitive abilities. Music therapy can offer maximum support and facilitate active participation for the client, enhancing their quality of life.

References

1. Folstein S. (1989). *Huntington's Disease: A Disorder of Families*. Baltimore: The Johns Hopkins University Press.

2. Harper P. (1991). The natural history of Huntington's Disease. In: *Huntington's Disease*. Harper P (ed). London: W. B. Saunders Company Ltd.

3. Shoulson I. (1990). Huntington's Disease: Cognitive and Psychiatric Features. *Neuropsychiatry, Neuropsychology, and Behavioural Neurology, 3(1)*: 15-22.

4. Rainey Perry M. (1983). Music Therapy in the Care of Huntington's Disease Patients. *Australian Music Therapy Association Bulletin; 6(4)*: 3-10.

5. Groom J & Dawes S. (1985). Enhancing the Self-Image of people with Huntington's Disease Through the Use of Music, Movement and Dance. *Proceedings of the 11th National Conference of the Australian Music Therapy Association Incorporated*, 66-67.

6. Erdonmez D. (1976). The Effect of Music Therapy in the Treatment of Huntington's Chorea Patients. *Proceedings of the 2nd National Conference of the Australian Music Therapy Association Incorporated*, 58-64

7. Hoskyns S. (1981). An Investigation of the Value of Music Therapy in the Care of Patients Suffering from Huntington's Chorea. Unpublished paper.

8. Curtis S. (1987). Music Therapy: A Positive Approach In Huntington's Disease. *Proceedings of the 13th National Conference of the Australian Music Therapy Association Incorporated*.

9. Dawes S. (1985a). The Role of Music Therapy in Caring in Huntington's Disease. In: *Handbook for Caring in Huntington's Disease*. Chiu & Teltscher (eds) Melbourne: Huntington's Disease Clinic.

10. Dawes, S. (1985b). Case study: Advanced Stage Huntington's Disease. *Proceedings of the 11th National Conference of the Australian Music Therapy Association Incorporated*, 87-92.

11. Tyler A. (1991). Social and psychological aspects of Huntington's disease. In: *Huntington's Disease*. Harper P (ed). London: W. B. Saunders Company Ltd.

Music Therapy with
Severely Head-Injured Clients

Catherine Durham
London, UK

Introduction

This chapter follows a year's work on the Brain Injury Unit at the Royal Hospital for Neuro-disability in Putney. This is a rehabilitation ward for those with profound brain injury, most commonly caused by trauma, heart attack or stroke. Admission takes place when the client is medically stable. This may occur many months post-injury; for example, after a road traffic accident where the victim sustains multiple injuries.

The multi-disciplinary team assigned to the ward consists of a consultant, specialist nurses, a neuropsychologist, a social worker, two occupational therapists and helper, two physiotherapists and helpers, a speech and language therapist and a music therapist. Also essential to many patients' rehabilitation are relatives and friends who can help carry out aspects of established programmes and provide emotional support to the patient. They supply useful information about aspects of a patient's personality and interests which may be incorporated into therapy programmes. The team aims to enable a patient to make more sense of the environment and to establish a communication system that will enable the person to express needs more fully. Often it will take many weeks for consistent 'yes' and 'no' signals to be developed. Suitable seating with specialised adaptations should be developed; essential for a person to be able to respond as fully as they can. The team aims to provide detailed recommendations for future care and management a person will require when discharged.

First I will outline the main types of profound brain injury and then summarise the place of music therapy within the multi-disciplinary team. The main body of the chapter consists of a case study of a young woman who has attended music therapy for twelve months. Following this will be a discussion of issues raised and an attempt to place this work within the context of palliative care.

Definitions of Typical States Following
Profound Brain Injury[1,2]

Brain-Death
Where no brain activity is present.

Coma
There exist a number of alternative terminologies. In the context of my work, I take coma to mean a state where arousal and awareness are not present. A patient will show no eye-opening, and reflexive movement only. There are myths surrounding the concept of coma. One is that people spend many years in this state. In fact it is rare for coma to extend beyond the duration of about six weeks. Another belief is that a patient will wake up and return to their 'normal' selves. In reality, when much of the brain has been damaged, emerging from coma will mean moving in to what is termed the 'vegetative state' or a state of severe or profound disability.

Vegetative State or 'Waking Coma'
Where a person shows wakefulness but no awareness. If this state persists for more than a year, the diagnosis often becomes the 'persistent vegetative state' [PVS]. Several people, however, have been known to emerge to a higher level of consciousness after a period of time. The diagnosis is not easy and is sometimes controversial.

Arousal
Even if a person shows arousal, (wakefulness is its most basic form) awareness may not be present. This is because arousal is a primitive brain function and can be activated by innate motivating systems such as hunger. Other factors such as 'vigilance' seem to be more important in achieving a state of awareness than arousal.[3]

Awareness
Where a person is shows some evidence of cognitive capacity; that is, thought. This implies there is integration of thought processes in the cerebral cortex. A patient is more likely to show movements that have some purpose.

Severe Brain Injury
Where a person shows some awareness but is severely disabled.

'Locked-In Syndrome'

Where cognition is completely or relatively unaffected, but due to damage to the brainstem the person affected is paralysed and therefore may have a very limited capacity to communicate with others. Even if someone has cognitive impairments, and is technically not 'locked-in', their lack of physical movement may mask what they are capable of in terms of comprehension of language, and other aspects of cognition. I have found it useful to bear this in mind as it clearly causes extreme frustration for some patients and great despair in others. For a summary of the Ranchos los Amigos scale of cognitive levels and expected behaviours for each level, see the Appendix. This gives an indication of how patients may progress as they move from the vegetative state to higher levels of awareness. Some patterns of recovery may however, differ.

Music Therapy on the Ward

The primary aim for my work is to attempt to address the emotional and communicative needs of the client through music. This frequently appears daunting, owing to the nature of each client. If a client begins to develop insight into their situation, they may become extremely agitated, or withdraw from communication with others. This withdrawal, combined with short-term memory problems makes building a trusting relationship between client and therapist, slow. I feel that it is important for the music therapist to have detailed knowledge of a client's physical and cognitive strengths discovered by other members of the team, combined with a sensntive and flexible approach.

As music bypasses language and is often a great motivator, music therapy can yield information about the amount of purposeful movement a newly admitted patient has. Music therapy is increasingly recognised as a medium for assessment, even though formalised tests are not applied. The playing of an instrument is more likely to encourage arm, finger or foot movement than the expectation of following an isolated command such as 'wave your hand'. There is also an immediate musical reward.

There are two music therapy groups that run weekly on the ward. Clients may be referred by any team member. Most therapists and nurses participate in the groups at least once in order to understand the criteria for referral.

The Music Awareness Group

This also involves an occupational therapist because of the need for one-to-one support. The sole criterion for inclusion in the group is that the client has shown a response to sound during the initial assessment. This group consists of only two or three clients, and is carefully structured (see case study for a detailed account). The musical activities provide maximum possibilities to participate with very carefully positioned instruments, although clients referred to this group tend to show very few observable responses and my assumption is that the richest aspect of their experience in the group is likely to be from listening, especially if the music matches their breathing patterns.

The Joint Therapy Group

This is so called because it receives input from three disciplines; music therapy, speech and language therapy and occupational therapy. All activities are based upon musical improvisation with a 'welcome' and 'goodbye' song for orientation framing the central activity. The criteria for referral for this group will be that most group members will have established a form of communication to indicate at least 'yes' and 'no', and most have the capacity to initiate movement on an instrument or can vocalise at will. The occupational therapist will have a good working knowledge of how best to facilitate a client to play an instrument, and the speech and language therapist has the most detailed knowledge of a client's comprehension and expressive abilities. She can advise on how best to present a choice of instruments to each person. We try to find out each individual's preference for timbre and volume if the instruments are electronically controlled with a switch. Often a preferred instrument is one that requires string plucking , such as an open-tuned guitar. This is because it requires minimal movement to produce sound. Many group members have restricted vision and visual-perceptual problems so the presence of different timbres in different parts of the room encourages awareness of others in the room space. Improvisations have been known to last up to fifteen minutes which is considerably longer than the period most clients would be expected to concentrate. The idioms used in the central improvisation vary from week to week; they can be structured or free. As the group traditionally consists mainly of young men, often the idiom most strongly responded to is rock or jazz, with preferred instruments being keyboards, drums, cymbals and guitars. The 'goodbye' song written for the group is based on a walking bass that I play on the cello.

Collaborative work is not always the most appropriate form of music therapy. Often I will work with people individually once or twice weekly if they show a particularly strong and positive reaction to music, or if music is the only medium in which they appear to show response.

Case Study: Anna

Background: Anna was twenty-eight years old when, pregnant with her first child, she became hypertensive which eventually caused an intracebral haematoma. After an emergency caesarian section in which a healthy boy was delivered, she went into coma. A craniotomy was performed to remove the haematoma. She showed little change after the operation.

Nine months later, when medically stable she was transferred to the Brain Injury Unit at Putney. As she was unable to move except for her eyes, she was seated in a specially adapted wheelchair with a headrest, and a headstrap around her forehead to prevent her head from falling. She also had severe leg contractures being unable to stand (even on a physiotherapy tilt-table). The contractures caused her considerable pain. She was completely dependent on nursing care and was gastrostomy fed. She did have strengths; she was able to breathe of her own accord, showed some ability to track objects and could control a slow blink, distinct from a faster reflexive blink.

Although she was unable to speak she was able to cry loudly which she did often; several times an hour. It was unclear whether this was triggered by pain, an extreme grief reaction or a neurological cause such as emotional lability. It seemed likely that it was a combination of all three factors.

Emotional lability is when a person laughs or cries in response to minor stimulation and has difficulty stopping. From accounts of other patients in the hospital who are able to communicate effectively, and who are also labile, they are often unable to stop crying even if they don't feel upset. People often ask to be distracted as they may feel embarrassed and out of control. Depending on the severity of lability, the response may be triggered by an increase in stimulation, such as someone speaking or a sudden loud noise.[4]

In Anna's case, I wondered whether her suspected lability was interfering with a more essential need to grieve. Alternatively, she may not have been labile and was using her crying as her only communication. The crying made other patients distressed resulting in Anna being withdrawn from various therapy groups and often from the general ward environment. It was also wearing for relatives and staff members.

Anna was referred to music therapy by the occupational therapist who intuitively felt that Anna was able to interact more was apparent.

Other factors that showed she might be suitable for music therapy were:

- A need for emotional expression
- A place where crying was acceptable
- She responded consistently to auditory stimulation

Music therapy was divided into three main stages:

- Music as sensory regulation in the Music Awareness Group
- Individual music therapy
- Group work focusing on awareness of others

For the first twelve sessions we met weekly for half-an-hour with one other patient and the occupational therapist. The session always took the same form:

- Verbal orientation where the time, date, year and place were explained.

- Greeting song containing a gap for any patient response to communicate 'hello', and providing a way of reminding us of each other's names.

- Presentation of single distinct musical sounds, always only two and of a contrasting nature. The instruments looked distinct from each other. Because of the position of Anna's head I usually had to hold the instruments in the air so as to be in her line of vision. Any response was carefully monitored.

- Farewell song to a familiar tune (Frere Jacques) using an autoharp tuned to D major which we held against Anna's hand in case she could feel the vibrations.

The central activity needed to be simple because with severe brain damage a person may lose the capacity to attend selective sound. Any background noise may distract attention away from the instrument presented. Two or more sounds simultaneously could also be confusing.[3]

Anna showed interest in the windchimes and tracked them particularly well. In the greeting song I prompted her to blink slowly in the appropriate gap. After four sessions she was able to do this within a few seconds of the prompt. By the end of eight weeks she was able to blink slowly without a prompt. This was clear evidence of learning.

At times Anna was able to concentrate in sessions for several minutes at a time. I began to present a choice of two instruments but she was unable to indicate which she preferred by looking at one or the other, tending to fix always on the first instrument presented.

After twelve weeks I began to work with Anna individually. She now appeared to recognise me. In these sessions I hoped to encourage more active participation than in the sensory stimulation sessions. The orientation, 'hello' and 'goodbye' songs remained, but for the central part of the session I used improvisation of single notes and phrases in response to slow eye blinks from Anna. This began as musical 'reinforcement', but began to evolve into a more creative musical interchange. A brief summary of the individual sessions highlights the significant changes.

In the first individual session Anna blinked at the appropriate point in the greeting song. She also blinked slowly at the end of each of four phrases improvised by me in sequence. In effect, she was blinking to indicate that she wishes the music to continue. In the second session, she cried whenever I spoke, but did not cry during the music. In the third session she initiated slow eye blinks at the beginning of the session without any prompts. She also cried at any lapse in the improvised music.

There followed a four-week gap as Anna had an operation at another hospital to have her achilles tendons cut. This operation would allow her to stand on a tilt-table, despite severe contractions in her ankles, which would be generally beneficial for her health. Anna also started taking Fluoxetine as a medication to treat her lability.

The following three music therapy sessions took place when Anna was confined to bed. Anna made good eye contact and despite a month's lack of therapy, was able to blink at appropriate points in the music without prompts. Despite frequent painful spasms which caused her to

191

cry, she was able to concentrate for several minutes at a time. By the third of these sessions she was choosing different instruments by looking at them.

After re-seating in a wheelchair, Anna began to make more rapid change. She began to hum quietly during the greeting song, and also turned her head to the right spontaneously. This was the largest purposeful movement I had seen. In the following session, Anna did not cry but used her right thumb to pluck an autoharp when it was held in position.

By the 21st session, Anna's crying was expressive and angry. Her vocal range had increased. She extended her thumb when I presented a plectrum for the autoharp which she then managed to grip. The speech and language therapist observed the next session and commented that it was the first evidence she had seen indicating that Anna had any comprehension of language.

Each session began to show positive change. One improvisation I played on the cello was sustained by Anna blinking after each phrase, for 15 minutes, five times longer than in early sessions. Anna's husband asked to attend one session. Anna was very attentive as if to show her husband proudly what she could do. She blinked slowly every time the word 'hello' was sung. Her husband played the autoharp in response to Anna's slow blinking. If he missed a blink, Anna cried immediately. Her husband noticed that Anna's contracted hands relaxed during the cello improvisations.

In the following session, Anna, alone again with me pushed her head out from under the headstrap and moved it from side to side in response to the music's pulse. Her blinking had become more complex; she would blink very hard and long if she wanted the music to continue, but during an improvisation on the cello, the blinks were shorter and generally synchronised to the main beats of the music. I tried many different speeds and idioms with her. Physically, she found it difficult to move to a fast pulse, and appeared to be most relaxed during modal improvisations in 3/4 time, which encouraged a gentle rocking of her head.

When she cried I would match the pitch of her crying with my voice, following the fall of her voice. This was also possible on the cello. This tended to result in her breathing in longer phrases for a few breaths, and then stopping to look at me before blinking slowly to begin the music again. We continued to work together on this basis until the 26th session.

When Anna celebrated her thirtieth birthday. Her husband gave her an autoharp.

Soon after this I referred Anna to the Joint Therapy Group with four other members in which she is now able to use her own autoharp and direct the group music using her eye blinks. She continues to cry, but this does not result in being removed from the group, and she is beginning to develop more control over when she cries and when she stops.

Anna had an initial diagnosis of being 'vegetative'. The way she responded during music therapy showed that this was far from accurate; she had the capacity to learn, and was responding in an increasingly creative way to the music. She clearly had awareness and vigilance. The study also illustrates how much change can occur during a short period of rehabilitation. It is difficult to assess how much of this change was due to spontaneous recovery and how much was due to the music therapy. Music therapy did however, appear to provide an environment where recovery could be shown to be happening. This is important in itself; if any of the team members are able to report positive change in a client's responses funding may be extended, or a different final placement may be recommended.

Anna is to be placed in a nursing home near to her family home and recommendations have been made to ensure the continuation of music therapy provision.

Issues Raised for the Therapist
Despite the fact that I have described work within a rehabilitative setting, I am increasingly convinced that much of this work is palliative in nature. As shown in the case study, music therapy can be used as a means to alleviate distress and pain. Anna could use music to distract herself from pain. The sessions gave her a sense of orientation and an escape from excessive passivity. She was taking control of the music in the sessions despite limited movement because of quadroplegia.

Although brain-injured clients are not facing death, they are experiencing irreversible change in their lives, and irretrievable loss. There is a need to work through anger and despair if the client is able to develop insight into their condition. It was impossible to know if Anna developed any knowledge of her situation, but she was able to feel the pain of her loss. Whenever communication was lost in the sessions she was able to express anger or sadness by crying. Her responses increased and diversified over time as she was able to develop a repertoire of expression within the musical context.

Both Anna and I were able to sense progress and therefore achievement, always a goal in a rehabilitative setting. This is not always possible. It is very easy as a therapist to fall into a tired pattern of working when spending many days with minimally responsive clients. When closer contact is made, it is invariably so intense an experience that the contrast between this and previous uneventful sessions can be enough to prevent the therapist from retaining any sense of containing the situation. The contact may become unbearable at times. The therapist also has the knowledge that a client used to be as active as he or she, and may therefore need to contend with their own feelings about the loss their client has suffered. This compares with some of the very intense feelings a therapist working with a dying person contends with.

After severe brain injury, life-expectancy for a client is reduced, and it is quite common for a client to die unexpectedly. Therapists cannot help prepare a client for an unexpected death and can be quite shocked when it happens. Because of the intensity of music therapy sessions in this setting, it is important to keep therapeutic boundaries. It is also essential to schedule team timetabling sessions to ensure that each client has a balanced day with plenty of rest periods.

When working with people who require detailed observation it is important not to schecule too many sessions in order to allow time for preparation and reflection. As music therapists who work with the dying attest, the therapist must be realistic about how deeply the work is affecting them personally, and ensure that they do not become overloaded or 'burned-out'. The nature of some of the communication between client and therapist feels primitive, particularly if it is based around eye contact and breathing only. As most of the clients on the ward are fully dependent for all aspects of nursing care, it is tempting to relate to them more as a mother does to a young infant. Most team members admit to having strong feelings of protectiveness towards some clients. The issues of respect and dignity have a particular significance in these instances: we are still working with adults, not babies.

If the therapist finds the change in the patient from their pre-trauma existence difficult to bear, the burdens family members and friends carry will be of an altogether different magnitude. Therefore, although the first loyalty of the therapist is to the client there are times when the families can benefit from some time spent with the therapist, talking about how their relative is changing. For Anna, her husband found a way in which he could make a meaningful gift to his wife, and opened up communication with his wife on her terms. There is clearly some potential for more family work to be developed in this context.

In terms of music therapy techniques used with severely brain-injured clients, please refer to the article by Aldridge et al[5] which describes music therapy practiced with comatose patients actively focussing on breathing patterns in an attempt to orient the patient to themselves.

The music therapist in any rehabilitative setting works within the multi-disciplinary team as mentioned earlier. This includes the providing and receiving of support amongst team members. Alongside this is the need for a personal style of working which is flexible enough to adapt to the needs of profoundly distressed or withdrawn patients, and I find that constant re-evaluation of my own values and assumptions when working with this client group are useful. I hope that this paper will provide a small insight into some of the issues those working in palliative care are concerned with.

Appendix

Rancho Levels of Cognitive Level and Expected Behaviour
This identifies a patient's highest level of cognitive functioning.

1. **No Response**
   Person appears to be in a deep sleep and is completely unresponsive to any stimulus presented to them.

2. **Generalised Reponse**
   Person reacts non-purposefully and non-specifically to stimuli. Responses are the same regardless of stimulus presented, e.g. mass flexion pattern. Responses may be gross body movement, vocalisation, or a change in breathing pattern. Responses may be delayed and inconsistent.

3. Localised Response

Patient reacts specifically to stimulus but the response is inconsistent. Responses are related to the particular stimulus; e.g. tracking of objects with eyes, withdrawal from light touch. Person may follow simple commands but in a delayed or inconsistent way, and may show ability to distinguish between people, so that responses may be greater towards family and friends.

4. Confused - agitated

Heightened state of activity with reduced ability to process information. Person reacts primarily to own internal confusion therefore behaviour appears non-purposeful as relating to the immediate environment.

May cry out in exaggerated response to stimuli. May show aggressive behaviour and attempts to remove restraints and tubes. Frequently unable to co-operate directly with treatment efforts. Vocalisation inappropriate to environment. Gross attention to environment is brief, and selective attention is often non-existent.

5. Confused - inappropriate

Person appears alert and responds to commands fairly consistently. With lack of external structure and with complex commands, response is non-purposeful. Demonstrates agitated behaviour out of proportion to external stimuli. Shows gross attention to environment, is easily distractible and lacks the ability to attend to specific tasks without frequent redirection. Lacks initiation and often shows inappropriate use of objects.

LEVELS 2 AND 3 CORRESPOND TO PVS. THE LEVELS SHOWN CORRESPOND TO THOSE GENERALLY EXPERIENCED BY PATIENTS ON THE BRAIN INJURY UNIT, PUTNEY.

References

1. MacLennan DR (1990). 'The Structural Basis of Coma and Recovery'. *Physical Medicine & Rehabilitation*; *4(3)*: 389-407.

2. Berrol S (1990). 'Persistent Vegetative State'. *Physical Medicine & Rehabilitation*; *4(3)*: 559-568.

3. Wood RL (1991). Critical Analysis of the Concept of Sensory Stimulation for patients in Vegetative State'. *Brain Injury*; *5(4)*: 401-409.

4. Sloan RL, Brown KW & Pentland B (1992). 'Fluoxetine as a treatment for emotional lability after brain injury'. *Brain Injury*; *6(4)*: 315-319.

5. Aldridge D, Gustorff D, Hannich H-J (1990). 'Where am I? Music therapy applied to coma patients'. *Journal of the Royal Society of Medicine*; *83*: 345-346.

Part Seven

Improvisation

Transcription of an Improvisation from a Session with a Client Living with HIV

Colin A Lee
Oxford, UK

Introduction
This paper provides the complete score of an improvisation (piano four-hands) from an individual session in music therapy with a client with HIV. My presentation at the conference included three extensive audio extracts (session eight - extract ten minutes, nine - extract twenty minutes and ten - extract ten minutes) from ten sessions with a young bereaved client. After a brief background describing the client and the referral procedure, the overall music therapy process was explained. This was followed, directly before each extract, by a description of the music the listener was about to hear. I provided no interpretation of the music nor did I indicate how the improvisations had affected the direction of the work. The presentation tried to highlight the intensity of exploring issues of death and loss within a musical framework without assessment. Hopefully the examples presented allowed the listener the opportunity to hear the therapeutic building-blocks directly through the musical experience.

In attempting to provide a similar record within the proceedings themselves (financial constraints did not allow for audio examples to be included) I decided to present a complete transcript of an improvisation taken from a previous piece of research.[1] The following notes provide the initial questions raised by the conference presentation, some basic information on the client, the stage of the therapeutic process reached, and the notational procedures used. The reader is ultimately left to draw their own conclusions as to the efficacy of the music, the therapeutic relationship and the possible connections between them.

Questions
Controversy arose from the paper and subsequent comments provided by conference delegates:

201

- What can be learnt from presenting the musical components of music therapy without assessment?

- What special qualities are there in improvisation for people facing either bereavement or a terminal diagnosis?

- Does music therapy need to include verbal interpretation to make its process valid?

- If we believe that the musical experience is vital in the therapeutic relationship, can music provide enough information to make the process clear?

- By presenting the music without a context clearly defined in depth, is there a danger that the musical experience may detract from the original validity of the study?

The varying responses to what might appear an extreme approach to the presentation of music therapy in palliative care came from a deeply ingrained belief in the potential of music to be illuminating without interpretation. A study of the philosophy of 'functional analysis',[2] where music is explained in terms of itself, became crucial in clarifying my own attempts to de-mystify the need for verbal analysis in music therapy. If 'functional analysis' ultimately fails it is perhaps because of the analyst's inability to let go of the intellectual restraints so ingrained in academic study. It could be suggested that the parallels in music therapy also stem from a need to articulate and understand the process in terms of outside models firmly based in verbal assessment. Recent publications now appear to be addressing similar issues. Ansdell[3] suggests that the answers to the enigmas of music are not necessarily to be found in words, and that to understand music therapy we need to understand the properties at the heart of music itself. By arguing that there is a need to explore the aesthetic qualities of music therapy, Aigen[4] suggests a view balancing previous medical and psychotherapeutic approaches to music therapy. I believe this return to focussing on the inherent beauty of music and its therapeutic value I believe is long overdue. Finally, in terms of research, the development toward qualitative methodologies[5] would suggest a more sympathetic approach to the potential exploration of the musical components in music therapy. Through my own studies of the analysis of improvisation[1,6,7] I have become convinced of the need constantly to re-evaluate the qualities of music in terms of the therapeutic relationship. Within palliative care musical dynamics become ever more present and real. It was these powerful experiences gained from my own clinical work that ultimately gave me the impetus to present my work in this form.

Session Extract

Number of sessions - 45
Transcription extract - session 21

The session lies at the midpoint of the therapeutic process.[8] It was clear at this stage that the client had refined the boundaries of both musical and therapeutic expression and the ever-shifting balance between them. There were sessions of clarity and insight that moved toward a therapeutic emphasis based essentially in music. Words became less important as the musical intensity heightened. The following comments demonstrate the client's clarity in the musical intention of the improvisations at this time:

> *"The anger that I feel, which is portrayed musically in a mainly disjointed fashion, is to do with my fears of the illness and the possible repercussions for me. I can express my fears through the music without actually having to spell them out verbally."*

The session in question consisted of three improvisations:

1. Percussion (including piano). Client and therapist

2. Piano four-hands. Client - bass, therapist - treble

3. Piano four-hands. Client - treble, therapist - bass

This combination was representative of the sessions at this time. The third improvisation is the score included in this paper.

Transcription

The music was transcribed via a Yamaha MIDI-Grand Piano.[9] Timing, in seconds, is placed at regular intervals on the score. The following three notational procedures are necessary for the understanding of the transcription:

1. *Metric regularity.* A suggested time-signature is notated in brackets.

2. *Metric irregularity.* No time-signature can be established. Dotted lines denote divisions of musical structure.

3. *Literal delineation.* X denotes those passages where all individual and associated themes are notated without a fixed structure. It is not necessary for any one part to correspond to another rhythmic component.

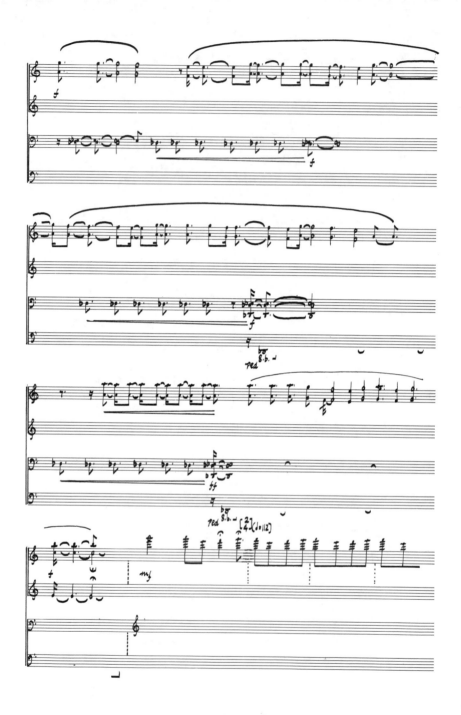

208

209

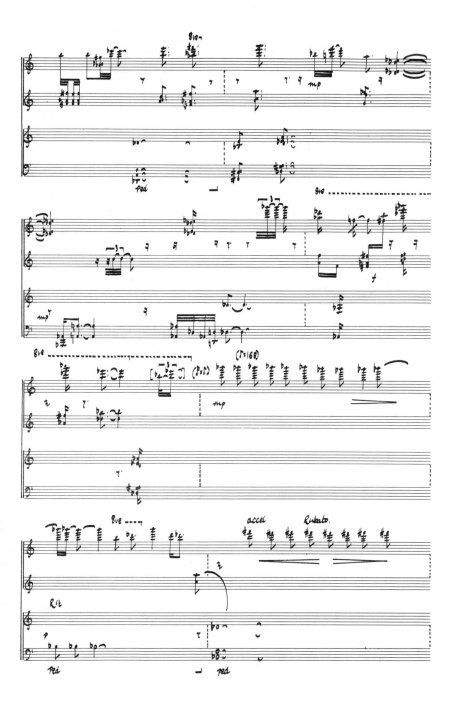

211

212

214

215

216

217

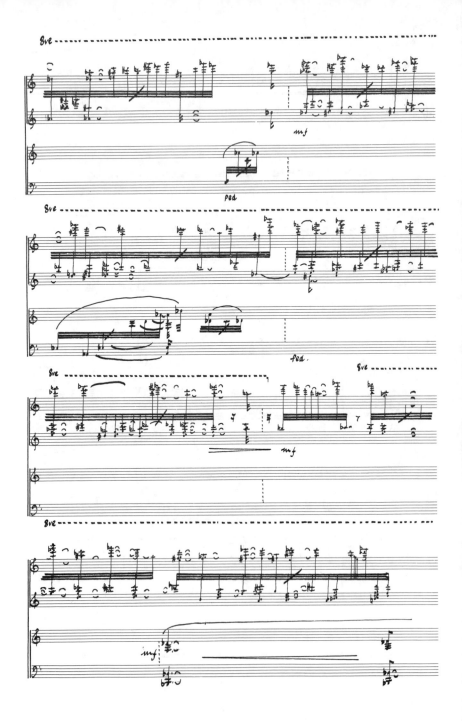

221

222

224

accel poco a poco/cresc poco a poco.

226

227

228

229

230

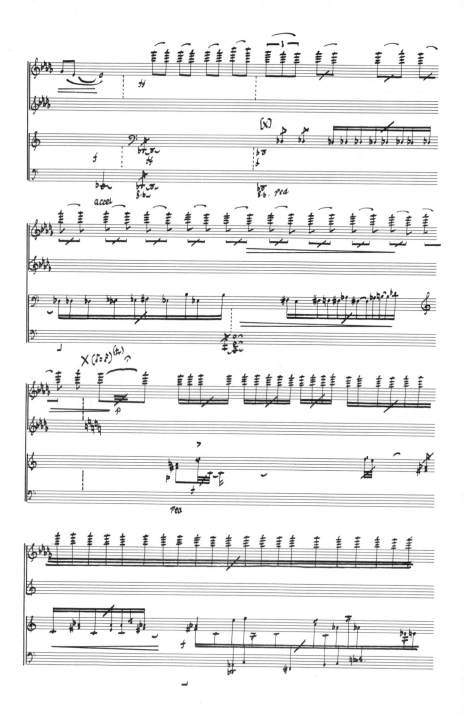

234

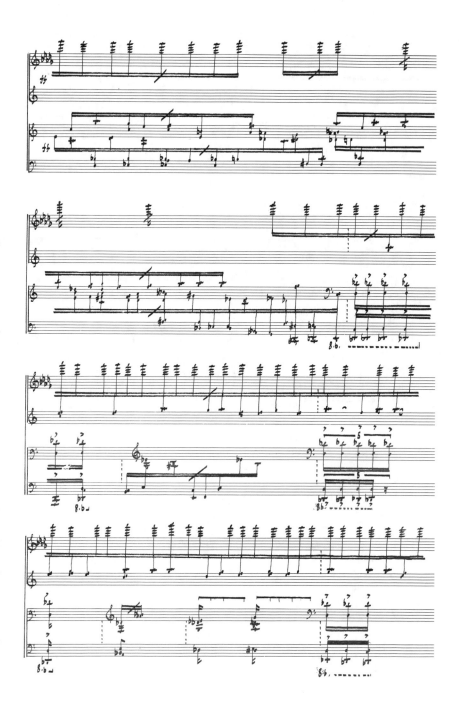

235

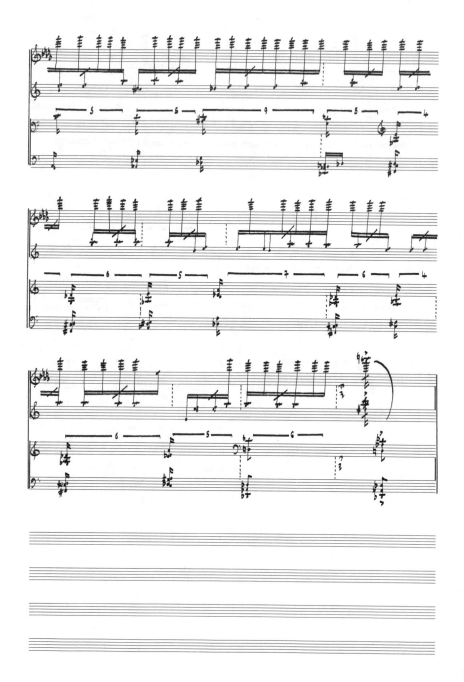

Concluding Comments

It is hoped that the reader will study the score both in terms of itself (as music) and in the context of music therapy in palliative care. Whilst it was not my intention to interpret the music, this does not preclude others from making assumptions about its validity. The purpose of this paper was simply to show the power of musical expression in the face of death and dying. The score contains intricate passages as well as sections that are simple and direct. The communication and relationship between players is complex yet honest. If in essence this presentation fails to communicate the most essential dynamic of music therapy, yet at its most fundamental level it has made a plea for the acceptance of music in music therapy as itself within itself.

References

1. Lee CA (1992). The Analysis of Therapeutic Improvisatory Music with People Living with the Virus HIV and AIDS. Unpublished PhD thesis, City University, London.

2. Keller H (1994). *Essays on Music*. Wintle (ed). Cambridge University Press.

3. Ansdell G (1995). *Music for Life. Aspects of Creative Music Therapy with Adult Clients*. Jessica Kingsley Publishers, London and Philadelphia.

4. Aigen K (1995). An Aesthetic Foundation of Clinical Theory: An Underlying Basis of Creative Music Therapy. In: Kenny (ed). *Listening, Playing, Creating: Essays on the Power of Sound*. (pp 233-257). State University of New York Press.

5. Bruscia K (1995). The Process of Doing Qualitative Research. In: Wheeler (ed). *Music Therapy Research. Quantative and Qualitative Perspectives*. (pp 389-443). Barcelona Publishers, Philadelphia.

6. Lee CA (1989) Structural Analysis of Therapeutic Improvisatory Music. *Journal of British Music Therapy*; *3(2)*: 11-19.

7. Lee CA (1990). Structural Analysis of Post-Tonal Therapeutic Improvisatory Music. *Journal of British Music Therapy*; *4(10)*: 6-20.

8. Ansdell G (1995). Case-study 'Charlie'. (pp 113-119). In: *Music for Life. Aspects of Creative Music Therapy with Adult Clients*. Jessica Kingsley Publishers, London and Philadelphia.

9. Lee CA (1995). The Analysis of Therapeutic Improvisatory Music. In: Gilroy & Lee (eds). *Art and Music: Therapy and Research*. (pp 35-50). Routledge, London and New York.